BUILD YOUR OWN METAL WORKING

THE CHARCOAL FOUNDRY

Written & Illustrated

By

DAVID J. GINGERY

printed in U. S. A.

LIBRARY OF CONGRESS CATALOG
CARD NUMBER 80-66142

ISBN 1-878087-002

DAVID J. GINGERY
SPRINGFIELD, MO.

Special thanks to Fine Woodworking magazine for permission to reprint Jack Fuller's classic cartoon of the home foundry operator, gone berserk.

Thanks also to Nick Tyler of Manotick, Ontario canada for calling the cartoon and the magazine to my attention.

Fine Woodworking magazine is published by Taunton Press, Inc., 52 Church Hill Road, Box 355, Newtown, CT 06470. A very good project oriented magazine that can be a great aid as you build your shop.

CONTENTS

THE METHODS AND MATERIALS THAT ARE SUGGESTED IN THIS MANUAL WERE DEVELOPED BY A NON-PROFESSIONAL. THE AUTHOR IS NOT AN ENGINEER OR SCIENTIST. NO LIABILITY IS ASSUMED FOR INJURY TO PERSONS OR PROPERTY THAT MAY RESULT FROM THE USE OF THIS INFORMATION.

FOREWORD

This second edition of this simple manual comes after the fifth printing of the first edition. The response to the first edition has been a very pleasant surprise, and the many letters from readers have been a help and inspiration. It seems appropriate to pass on the benefit of these first three years of experience, and to offer my thanks for such an enthusiastic response.

There is a great deal that can be said about metal casting that will not be found in these pages, for the object is to describe a foundry operation in its most basic form. There is nothing new or revolutionary in the methods or materials presented here. In fact, the entire approach is to be through long forgotten methods that were in use before the advent of space age technology. If you were to attempt to set up a foundry with todays methods and materials, it would likely be beyond your reach as a hobby or a home based activity. There is ample room to grow when you have seen how easy it is to produce castings by these simple means.

Keep in mind that you are working with high temperature, and be aware of the danger to yourself and your property. Establish a safety plan and follow your plan as you work.

INTRODUCTION

The more than 20 years of research and experimentation that precede this group of manuals was inspired by a statement by someone I've long forgotten: " The metal lathe is the only machine in the shop that can duplicate itself or any other machine in the shop. " It followed then: If you have a lathe you can produce the rest of the needed equipment to make up a fully equipped machine shop.

Of course my first problem was that I didn't have the lathe. As is usually the case with the hobbiest, experimenter or inventor, I didn't need a machine shop, I just wanted one. There was no way to justify the cost of the commercially made equipment so I set out to build my own.

The theme of the idea is remarkably like the recipe of someones grandmother for chicken soup, which begins " First you get a chicken. ". Well, if you want to make chicken soup you'll have to buy a chicken. Or, lacking the necessary funds, you might steal one. You can't make a chicken, but you can build your own lathe, and with it you can produce the rest of the equipment to make up a full and practical machine shop.

The photo on the previous page is of the lathe that was built as this series of manuals was being prepared. It has a 7" swing with 12" between centers. A split nut drives the carriage automatically through the powered lead screw, and change gears are added later to give full thread cutting capability. All of the castings are made with the simple charcoal foundry, and the remainder of the parts are standard hardware items. The only power tool used was a 3/8" electric drill, and there was no custom machine work of any kind. The lathe can not only duplicate itself, it can actually build itself. All of the machine work was done on the machine itself as it progressed step by step. When it was complete I used it to build another just like it. This was followed by a 6" metal shaper, a milling machine, a drill press, a worm wheel dividing head, and finally a four jaw chuck and a set of change gears for thread cutting. Of course all of the tooling and fixtures were made with the machines themselves as they developed. Not one dime was spent on custom work outside my shop. You can do it too, and it's easy with the charcoal foundry.

My early attempts at building machine tools were not very successful. While I was able to build something near what I wanted it was never quite satisfactory. The main problem was in the alignment of the parts in relation to each other. (A vital factor if you hope to achieve reasonable precision in your work.) I was attempting to make up the parts as weldments and to assemble them on beds and ways welded up of stock cold rolled steel. Of course it never turned out as I planned. The expansion and contraction of the metal as it was heated and cooled would misalign the parts, and it was a messy and tedious business.

It wasn't until I had acquired a bushel of worn out hack saw blades, a lot of broken drills and taps and a big mound of scrap iron that I realized that the secret of success was in using castings instead of weldments. It solved the problem of producing parts, and it opened a new world of experience in metal working that gave real purpose to the rest of my efforts. The savings in time, labor and money are so great that I am amazed that the idea did not occur earlier.

I spent the entire first winter trying to design a gas furnace that was tame enough for the amateur and hot enough to do the job. Several worked, but all of them were wild and noisy. They all had to be started with an oil soaked wad. This works well enough, but eventually the wad comes out the vent in the form of very dangerous and smelly bits of burning rag. It was necessary to attend the furnace continually in case it lost ignition, and the pulsation and roar were a distraction. All together it was a risky business, and I feel fortunate that my garage is still standing so that I have a place to pursue my hobby.

The charcoal furnace proved so simple to build and use that I decided to design the entire series of machine projects around the capacity of this simple solid fuel furnace.

Many people are amazed to learn that charcoal could produce a fire hot enough to melt metal. The fact is that in the early history of foundry work, charcoal was the main fuel. There was a great deal of iron smelted in this country in charcoal fired cupolas, and entire communities were built around the activity. St. James, Missouri is one example where iron ore was mined, charcoal was made from native wood, and the air blast was furnished by twin leather bellows that were powered by a water wheel. It was a small town, and the company even printed its own money in the form of script, for which they got into some trouble with Uncle Sam. The town is gone now, but the shaft of the cupola remains along with remnants of some of the equipment. There is a museum with a scale model of the operation as it was, and Merimac Springs, which furnished the water power for the wheel is now a trout hatchery, and a popular tourist attraction in the area. There are many such examples all over the country, and charcoal will burn as hot today as it did 100 years ago.

The use of solid fuel has another advantage in that if you don't have gas available in your work area it can be a matter of considerable trouble and expense to install it. In some localities it may not even be permitted at all.

The investment of time and money in the charcoal foundry is so slight that if you try it and decide that foundry work is not for you, you will not be distressed at the small amount you will have spent.

It should be pointed out that these methods have little commercial value. This is not the right equipment if you intend to produce castlngs in quantity, though it is very appropriate for one of a kind jobs. It is a very good way to learn the fundamentals of foundry work and to produce the castings for building your machine shop. There is no thrill to compare with shaking a new casting out of the sand, and no metal worker should deprive himself of the experience.

CHAPTER I

FOUNDRY WORK IN GENERAL

A PRIMITIVE ART

In simple terms, foundry work involves pouring molten metal into a mold cavity of the desired shape and size. The result is a duplicate in metal of the pattern used to make the mold. It is a simple art that has been practiced for centuries. Primitive people with simple means were able to turn out useful items in cast metal, and their resources were nothing more than sand, clay ore and charcoal. With little more than this we can turn out the necessary castings to build our own machine tools. You will shortly see that you don't have to buy a lot of expensive and complicated equipment to produce your own castings. It is likely that you will acquire much of what you need at no cost at all, and such as you must buy costs but little.

GREEN SAND MOLDING

There are many ways to make a mold for a casting, but of all of them, green sand molding is the most practical for the beginning, small home operation. It is easy to learn, the cost is small, and the rewards are great. If your first attempt to make a mold fails, you just make it over again, using the same material. Nothing is lost but a little dust and a few minutes of time. How's that for economy.

The sand is not green in color. The term means that the mold is not baked or cured before the molten metal is poured in. The sand you use will range in color from tan to brown, or even black, for many things can be added to the sand to give it properties that it does not possess in its natural state.

Other processes, such as investment molding and shell molding, require that the mold must be fired in a kiln before filling with molten metal. Still others use chemical binders, and they are cured with heat or catalysts. These all have their proper use, but they require equipment that is generally too costly and too technical for most of us. I will leave it to others to instruct you in more exotic methods, and we'll concentrate on what I believe to be the easiest and most rewarding method of metal casting.

8

If you have ever built sand castles or made mud pies, you have some experience in green sand molding. It really is that easy. The sand that we use is silica sand that contains clay as a binder. When it is properly conditioned it will take an impression of the pattern and provide a cavity into which we pour the molten metal.

Some detail has been left out in order to demonstrate simple principle, but we'll go into that a little later. The sand, rammed into a flask over a pattern, makes the mold. Into the mold we pour the moten metal.

MAKE YOUR OWN EQUIPMENT

In addition to a supply of sand, fire-clay, charcoal, scrap metal and some parting dust, you will need molding equipment and a means to melt the metal. These are simple items that we'll discuss as we move along. Basic supplies are not costly, and we'll mention some sources at the end of the book for those items that can be purchased. For a portion of what is needed you must find and devise substitutes for the commercial product because they are not easily available to individuals in small quantity. I'm not going to send you out in a loin cloth to mine the ore with a sharp stick and break it up with a stone hammer, but some of the methods and substitutes are at least old fashioned if not down right primitive.

The molding equipment consists of flasks and various small hand tools that are mostly made of wood. The flasks are little more than wooden boxes without bottoms or tops, and they are easily made.

The patterns are made of wood, plastic, metal or anything that you can tool into the desired shape. You can even use a broken part that has been temporarily mended to make a mold for a new casting. Simple wood working tools are all you need for pattern making.

The equipment for melting and handling the metal is so simple that you will have no problem in finding what you need to equip yourself. It is likely that you have some of it on hand right now.

The entire group of equipment can be stored in a very small space in the corner of your garage or shed. Most of what you need is easily made, and such as you might prefer to buy is not expensive.

Sit back now and enjoy your leisure, because next week you are going to be busy at work in your own foundry.

9

CHAPTER II

THE EQUIPMENT AND SUPPLIES

MOLDING SAND

The molding sand is probably the most important single item in the foundry. With the exception of pattern making, it will take more time and attention than any other single item in your home foundry. In commercial foundries the sand is all over the place. In piles, in bags, in hoppers, on the floor and where ever you look. It's not hard to see why molders used to be called " SAND CRABS ", because they spent their working lives crawling backwards through the stuff. With their faces and hands blackened with sea coal and plumbago they were not a handsome sight. For the home operation, you need just a couple hundred pounds of good molding sand and enough rough sand to make a 2" thick bed in the melting and pouring area. You won't get enough of it on you to spoil your good looks.

The sand that we use for molding is silica sand with clay as a binder. Other elements are often added to improve the quality, but simple sand with the right amount of clay will work very well for casting aluminum and pot metal. When it is found in deposits with the right proportion of clay it is called natural bonded sand. If clean sand is mixed with clay and other addatives it is called synthetic sand. The idea is to have enough clay in the blend to coat each grain so that they will stick together when moistened. Among the other addatives are sea coal and wood flour. The sea coal is pulverized bituminous coal, and it is used to form a gas film between the metal and the sand to prevent fusing the sand with the casting. This is not as important in aluminum and pot metal casting as it is with iron or steel because of the lower temperatures involved. The wood flour is used to improve the water absorbing quality of the sand, and it makes it more resilient. both elements make a very noticeable difference, but you can work without them if they are not available to you.

BUY IT IF YOU CAN

A couple of hundred pounds of molding sand may well be a lifetime supply, unless you do an awful lot of casting. It won't be a continuing expense, so if you can buy it at a local foundry or supply house, do so. I offered to buy a couple of hundred pounds of used sand from the dump pile at a local foundry, and the manager urged me to help myself to as many tons as I could use at no charge. I sifted out the rubble and ended up with some excellent sand for my purpose. You may be lucky too.

If you must have sand shipped in, the freight is likely to cost as much as the sand, and the expense begins to be prohibitive for the home operation. Then it pays to look for native sand or to blend your own synthetic sand.

Masonry sand is washed to remove clay and silt from it, but if you can buy it at the pit before it is washed it is likely that it will be good molding sand. It must be silica sand, and very fine grain size. Crushed lime stone or other soft crushed rock is not suitable for molding because it absorbs and holds water, and it will explode when it is heated by the molten metal. If you are in doubt about the nature of the sand it is a good idea to heat a sample with a torch to see if it will stand high temperature.

There is a white silica sand that is sold for use in sand blasters. An 85 mesh sand is fine enough, and it is about the same texture as extra fine granulated sugar. A 65 mesh sand is very noticeably more coarse, and though it will work the surface quality of your castings will suffer. This sand is often labeled " Foundry Sand ". It is foundry sand indeed, but it is not molding sand until it is mixed with clay to give it bond.

BLENDING SYNTHETIC SAND

Any silica sand that is fine enough, and is washed to remove silt and other organic matter, can be blended with clay to make molding sand. You can buy silica sand as described above in 100 pound bags, and you can also buy sand that is prepared for masonry work. Sand is graded by the mesh number, and the highest number is the finest grade. Aluminum casting sands are usually made from 75 mesh to 125 mesh sand. Below 75 mesh is considered too coarse, but 65 mesh will do in a pinch if you can't get finer. Buy a pound of extra fine granulated sugar as a comparison standard if you are not familiar with sand grades, or pay a visit to a local foundry to get a look and feel of molding sand in use.

There are many different kinds of clay, and the bonding quality varies greatly among them. Fire clay and bentonite clay will be the most easily available to you, and either

11

can be used to bond your sand. Sea coal and wood flour are likely to be hard to find, but you can use wheat flour, corn flour or corn starch as a substitute.

The sand and ingredients are mixed while absolutely dry, and you should wear a respirator mask to avoid inhaling any of the dust. Once it has been blended and tempered there is no longer any problem with dust.

It will require from 25% to 35% of fire clay by weight to bond clean silica sand. This ends up with an analysis of from 20% to 26% clay to the blend because the clay adds its weight to the mass. If you add 25 pounds of clay to 100 pounds of sand, the total mass will weigh 125 pounds, and the clay will represent 20% of the mass. The object is to add enough clay to coat each grain of sand to give good bond, but not so much clay as to close up the porousity of the sand blend. Begin with a small batch of a pound or two of sand and thoroughly mix in one fourth its weight in clay. Then temper the sample with water and allow it to stand for about 30 minutes before you test its bond. If it does not seem strong enough you can make a second test batch with a little more clay. You will soon reach a point where adding more clay does not improve the blend. Then you have the formula for the particular clay that is available to you.

Bentonite clay is so much better than fire clay that it requires only from 5% to 10% of it to give a better bond than fire clay. Experiment with it in the same manner as described for the fire clay until you arrive at the right proportion. Bentonite is sold by dealers in farm supplies for a number of uses. Its main use is probably for making feed pellets for live stock, and it is also used to seal the bottoms of farm stock ponds. You can buy it in 50 pound bags, and that will make a lot of molding sand.

When you have arrived at the proper proportion of clay you can mix up all of your sand in that proportion. Add from 1% to 1 1/2% of some type of flour to the dry mix. I have experimented with several kinds of flour and they all seem to produce about the same effect. Some types of wall paper paste that are sold in powder form seem to work just a little bit better than flours. Corn flour, corn starch, wheat flour, or very fine sanding dust from hard wood are the most likely choices for you. These improve the water absorption quality of the blend, and it seems to make the sand more resilient. Mix the flour with the clay, and then mix the blend with the sand very thoroughly while dry.

TEMPER THE SAND

When the sand is properly moistened for molding it is said to be " TEMPERED ". The water content in the blend has as much to do with its cohesiveness as does the clay. More water means better bond, but more than enough is too much. I know that sounds ambiguous. I speak foolishly to catch your attention on a very important matter.

Old sand crabs test molding sand by grabbing a hand full and squeezing it into a sausage shape. Then he breaks it in half to test the strength of the bond and to examine the texture. He will also compress it in his hand and blow through it to test its porousity. This is a matter of the acquired judgement that comes from experience. You will soon become familiar with the characteristics and faults of your sand, and these simple tests will have meaning to you.

The sample in the photo below is 85 mesh sand with 8% bentonite and 1% wheat flour. It feels slightly damp, but not wet. It felt resilient as I squeezed it into the sausage shape, and the imprint of my fingers was distinct. It broke in half cleanly without crumbling up. This is the condition you are trying to achieve as you temper the sand.

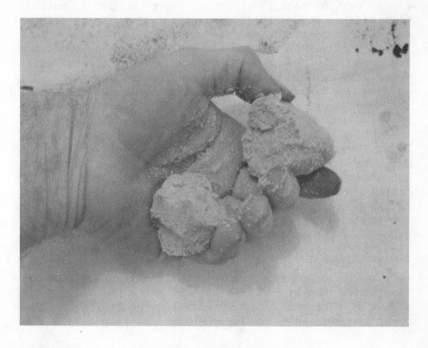

Only a very small amount of water is required to temper the sand. The total amount of moisture is going to be from 7% to 8%. There is certain to be some amount of water in any sand you work with, but you won't know how much. You will likely have to add somewhere in the neighborhood of 2% to 4% to newly blended sand. A quart of water weighs about 2 pounds, so if you add a quart to 100 pounds of sand you have raised the water content by about 2%. You may use about a gallon of water to temper a 200 pound batch of new sand.

A garden sprinkling can is ideal in the home shop. Just spread the sand out in your bin and sprinkle about a pint of water over the surface. Mix it up with a trowel and level it off to sprinkle on another pint. Mix it up again and pile it up on one end of the sand bin. Now shake the whole batch through the riddle. Give it the squeeze test to see if it needs more water, and repeat the whole operation if more water is added.

There is a tendency to add too much water to newly tempered sand because it takes time for the dry clay to absorb water and become plastic. Newly tempered sand will always feel better on the second day, so be content with a slightly dry feel on your first batch. Even an hour of waiting will make a noticeable difference, so give plenty of time before you decide to add more water.

If the sand is too dry it will crumble and break when you try to draw the pattern from the mold, and loose particles will wash into the mold. If it's too wet there will be an excess amount of steam when the molten metal enters the mold, and that is dangerous. It will spit and sputter as you pour, and the molten metal will bubble back out of the sprue. Don't try to complete the pour because the casting will be ruined anyway. An over wet mold or core can cause the mold to blow, and serious injury can result. A proper mold will make a sound no more violent than that of frying eggs, and the molten metal will lay quietly in the cavity until it solidifies.

If the sand is too wet you can mix in some dry sand to bring down the percentage of moisture, or leave it uncovered for a day so that some of the water will evaporate.

If you keep the sand covered with a sheet of plastic it will remain in condition for a long time. Each time you use it you should shake it back into the bin and add the amount of water to bring it back into condition. Then cover it up to be ready for your next casting session.

THE MOLDING BENCH

While you could just dump the sand on the floor, and do your molding while squatting, it will be found a real convenience to have a molding bench in which you can store the sand and do your molding while standing.

The suggested design will hold 200 pounds of sand at a convenient working height, and it's easy to cover when not in use. You could even build it outside if you provide a cover to keep out the weather and stray cats, who will not know that it is not intended as a litter box.

2" X 6" Lumber makes the sides and ends, and the bottom is 1/2" exterior glued plywood. The rails are 2" X 4", and they are joined with a couple of cleats nailed to the under side so that it can slide freely across the top of the bin.

The legs can be six standard concrete blocks in stacks of three, and they can be layed up dry or with mortar. The bin should be fastened to a wall so that it can't topple as you work.

A shelf on the wall at about eye level makes a convenient place for small tools and supplies. The furnace and the rest of your equipment can be stored underneath, so the entire foundry need not occupy more than a corner of your shop.

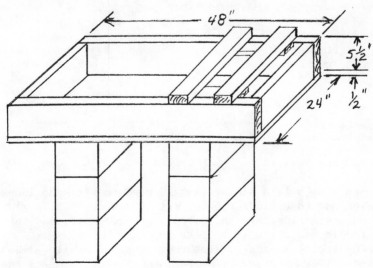

EXTENDED RAILS

Extended rails can be fastened to the top of the bin to aid you in rolling over larger flasks. The ends of the rails are rounded nicely so that you can rest the bottom board against them as you roll over to bring the molding board on top. With this method you can easily roll over a 50 pound flask without clamping the boards.

You just ram up the drag and rub in the bottom board. Then slide the whole thing off the rails and rest the bottom board against the end of the rails as you roll it back onto the rails in the inverted position. It only takes a little practice to master it.

The small amount of labor and expense that will be involved in the molding bench will quickly repay you in time saved in producing molds.

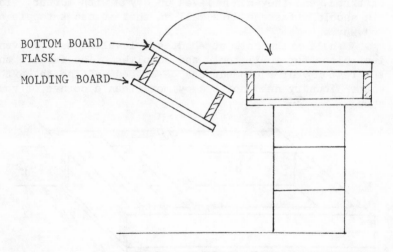

BOTTOM BOARD
FLASK
MOLDING BOARD

THE RIDDLE

The riddle is a sifter that is used to break up lumps of sand and to exclude rubble. It is also an aid in mixing and tempering the sand. You just scoop the sand into the riddle and shake it to sift the sand.

Commercially made riddles are a round hoop with a mesh bottom. They are sized by number, and the number means the number of meshes to the running inch. A number 4 riddle will have 4 meshes to the inch, or 1/4" squares. A number 2 riddle has 1/2" square mesh, and a number 8 has 1/8" mesh. I've recently found that a number 2 riddle is adequate for almost all of my work. A number 8 is too slow, and does little better than a number 2 or number 4.

Use the heaviest grade of mesh you can find, and fasten it to the bottom of the wooden frame with thin wood or metal strips. It's simply a wooden box with a mesh bottom.

The sand can be scooped into the riddle with an empty coffee can or an ordinary garden trowel.

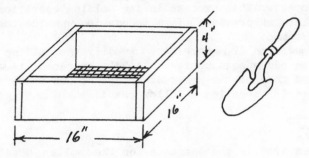

THE RAMMER

The traditional molders bench rammer is made of maple. It has a large blunt end from 3" to 4" in diameter, and the other end is a blunt wedge about 3" to 4" wide.

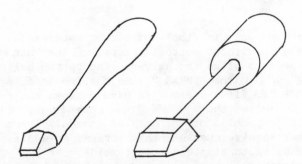

The wedge shaped end is used to drive the sand tightly into the corners of the flask and around the pattern, and the blunt end is used directly over the pattern where it is usually desired that it not be as tightly rammed. A good rammer can be made of a large hammer handle.

17

MOLDING BOARDS AND BOTTOM BOARDS

These are merely smooth flat boards that are near to the size of the flask being used. They need a coat or two of varnish or lacquer so they won't absorb water from the sand.

The pattern is placed on the molding board, the drag is inverted over the pattern, and the sand is rammed over the pattern and wedged securely into the drag. The bottom board is rubbed in over the drag sand, and the entire group is rolled over. This process in the molding operation beds the pattern and provides a firm foundation on which the cope sand is rammed.

ON occasion it is necessary to modify the molding board to use an odd shaped pattern. A hole or recess is cut in the board to accept a protruding part of the pattern. In this case it is called a follow board.

SPRUE PINS

These provide the entrance for the molten metal, and they can be of metal or wood. A length of pipe or tube, a dowel or broom stick, or even plastic tubing will serve.

They are sized according to the weight of the casting to be poured, and they are also used to provide risers and feeders for heavy sections. The general rule is that the sprue or riser should be larger in diameter than the thickness of the portion of the mold that they feed.

FLASKS

Molds are made in flasks of two or more parts. They resemble boxes without bottoms or tops, and they are fit with pins or pegs to align the halves. The bottom half of the flask is called the " DRAG ", and the top half is called the " COPE ". If a section is used between the cope and drag it is called the " CHEEK ". A cheek is used for some unusually deep molds or for complex shapes. There are no molds that require cheeks in this series, so we'll confine our discussion to simple two part molds.

A pattern will be layed on the molding board and the drag half of the flask is inverted over the pattern. The drag is rammed full of sand and struck off level, and the bottom board is rubbed in over the sand. Then the drag is rolled over and the molding board is set aside. This will expose the parting surface of the drag, and the bedded pattern will be seen. Then the cope half of the flask is set in place, to be rammed full of sand and struck off level. The filled cope is then lifted off and set aside so that the pattern can be drawn from the mold. When the pattern is drawn, the mold is again closed to pour in the molten metal. There are a number of steps that are not mentioned here, so that you can understand the function of the alignment pegs. They are installed so that the flask can be reassembled in exactly the same position after the pattern has been drawn from the mold. the joint between the cope and drag is the " PARTING " of the mold, and it must fit perfectly so that molten metal won't run out when the mold is poured. The pegs are designed to align the halves perfectly at the parting, but they must fit freely enough so that the mold can be opened without jarring the cope sand. Some patterns are split at the parting so that a portion will be in the drag, and the remaining portion will be in the cope. The importance of perfect register is apparent.

Commercially made flasks can be of steel, aluminum, wood or plastic. There are many types of flasks, and several methods of alignment at the parting. They are generally too expensive for home shop use, so you will likely want to make your own. The simple type shown here will serve for all of the requirements in this series of projects. You will need several sizes, and some will be special in some way. These will be described when the need arises. If you make one with inside measurements of 8" X 10", and another of 12" X 12" at this time, they will serve your needs until you begin a definite project. They will later be your most used sizes, so make them carefully.

If you make them of pine or other solid wood you can join them at the corners with glue and nails or screws. If you make them of plywood you should use solid wood cleats at the corners as shown in the drawing, because nails or screws will not hold well in the end grain of plywood. A sheet metal corner brace works out pretty well in place of the cleats if it is fastened to the outside of each corner.

The critical point in construction is the fit at the parting, so both halves must be of the same size and well squared at the corners. It's a good idea to assemble with just one nail or screw at each corner, and then align the halves together before you finish fastening the corners.

I make all of my flasks of pine, and I join them at the corners with glue and cement coated nails.

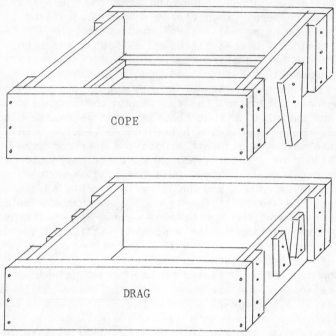

COPE

DRAG

Make each half of 3/4" X 3 1/2" stock, which gives a total flask depth of 7". Small flasks can be smooth inside, but the 12" X 14", and any flasks larger than 10" square, need a groove or a rib around the inside of the cope. 1/2" square stock can be nailed inside, or you can cut a 1/2" square groove before you assemble the parts. This is to prevent the cope sand from falling out when you open the mold to withdraw the pattern. The drag needs no rib, but it is a good idea to install one anyway, in case you use the flask upside down for a special job.

The taper of the pegs and sockets is shown exaggerated in the drawing to emphasize the importance. A taper of 1/4" over the length of the peg is adequate. The object it to have the flasks fit in perfect register when they are snug together at the parting, but they must separate easily so that the cope sand is not jarred when the mold is opened.

First make the flask halves and install the pegs on the cope. Then join the halves and install the sockets on the drag to fit the pegs closely. Set the peg and socket on one end off center so that the mold can only be assembled in one way. This will prevent setting the cope back in the wrong position after the pattern has been drawn.

It will be easiest to install the pegs and sockets accurately if you drill and screw them. I use a strip of 10 point bristol board between one side of the socket and the peg to provide clearance after sealing with varnish or lacquer. This will leave just a tiny bit of clearnace so that there is no binding when the mold is opened.

Make sure they fit closely and open smoothly, and then seal with two coats of varnish, paint or lacquer. Test the fit again when the sealer has dried thoroughly.

THE VENT WIRE

Molds are vented to release steam and gas. A stiff wire about 1/16" in diameter and about 6" long will serve. Form a loop on one end for a handle.

DRAW PEGS AND RAPPERS

A draw peg is screwed into a hole left in the pattern, and it is rapped all around to free the pattern from the mold. This enlarges the cavity a slight amount so that the pattern can be lifted out without damaging the cavity. The draw peg can be a screw eye or hook of convenient size, and the rapper can be a metal rod; or, you can cast one in pot metal or aluminum like that in the sketch. The forked design is of about 1/2" section thickness throughout, and it is very convenient to use because you can shake it back and forth against the peg as you rotate around it.

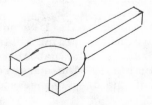

21

THE SWAB

Before you rap the pattern you swab all around the edge with a soft bristle brush dipped in water. This strengthens the bond to prevent breaking the edges of the cavity when the pattern is drawn. You also use the swab to wet any weak areas, and such places as the gates, runners or any area that threatens to break loose when the metal is poured into the mold. The bottom of the sprue is one area that should always be swabbed, and any sharp corners in the gates or runners should be rounded off with the wet swab. If a corner or edge breaks loose as you draw the pattern, you can usually touch it with the wet swab, and the water will pull the parts back together.

A large round camel's hair brush that will come to a point when wet makes a very good swab. You can fit soft bristles to the end of a small syringe to make what molders call a " BULB SPONGE ".

MISCELLANEOUS SMALL TOOLS

If there is minor damage to the mold cavity when you draw the pattern, you can usually repair it with a small trowel or spoon. Artists pallette knives and trowels make handy mold finishing tools, and so does old silverware that is cut and bent to whatever shape and size you need.

You can make a handy gate cutter by blunting the end of an old spoon and bending it to a trough shape. A narrow strip of sheet metal can be bent to a trough shape for the same purpose.

Small masons tools like pointing trowels and patching trowels are handy molding tools. A pointing trowel is of a diamond shape, and a patching trowel is about 1 1/4" wide with a blunt end. These are great for slicking up the parting face of the drag before you ram up the cope.

You'll be forced to use your imagination for fabricating your small molders tools. A stick, a piece of wire or a strip of sheet metal may well turn out to be your handiest tool. You can spit on the end of a stick and use it to lift a bit of loose sand from a mold cavity, or an old open end wrench might make a handy rapper. Study the problem, then use what you have and make it work.

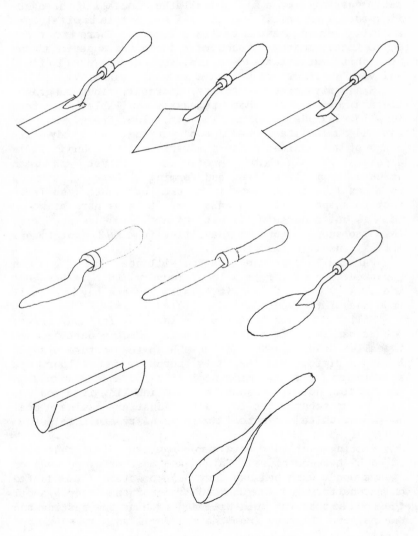

23

SUPPLIES

Very little is really required in the way of supplies in the home shop. I made my first molds with a sand blend made of play box sand, purchased at a discount store, and some red clay soil dug from my garden. Graphite was my parting dust, and I melted zink alloy in a cast iron skillet over a gas hot plate. This was all I used to pour a set of castings for a miniature lathe, and all of the castings turned out well. You can see how little is vital, and anything beyond these is really a luxury. There is not any doubt that commercial foundry products are superior to the make shift substitutes we devise, but they are hard to find, and very difficult to purchase in small quantity.

Sand, fire-clay, bentonite, charcoal, flour and graphite are common items that are easily available. Pattern supplies include varnish or lacquer, glue, brads, sand paper and common items used in wood working. Auto body putty is one of the handiest pattern materials I've found. It is a polyester resin that is cured with a catalyst, and it can be used for filling flaws and forming fillets. It sets up to a wax like consistency in just a few minutes, so it is easy to shape. Within a half hour it is as hard as wood, so it is quite durable for pattern use. You can buy it at any auto supply store in quantities from 1/2 pint to one gallon, and it's easy to use.

Parting dust is one item you will need, and if you can buy about 5 pounds from a local foundry, that is the best idea. If you can't find it locally you can buy it by mail from one of the sources to be listed later.

Silica flour was used for parting dust for many years, but it was found to cause silicosis. Modern parting dust is called " NON-SIL ", and it is high temperature plastic flour. Diatomaceous earth is amorphous silica flour. It is sold for use in swimming pool filters, and it can be used for parting dust. Be sure to avoid inhaling it if you use it. Other substitutes for parting dust are pumice or coal dust. Graphite works too, but it is nasty stuff to get on you.

Parting dust must be a non-absorbent flour that will stand high temperature. Talcum and most other powders or flours won't work because they absorb water. It is dusted on the pattern and the parting face of the drag to spoil the bond so that the mold will separate at the parting and the pattern releases from the mold. A sock makes a good dusting bag for parting.

THE SHOP AIR SUPPLY

You need a supply of compressed air for blowing loose particles of sand and dust from the mold. You will likely be tempted to huff it away with lung power, but you risk inhaling the dust which will soon destroy your health. Use a bellows or a pistol handled hair dryer or other low pressure air supply to protect your lungs and eyes.

You can purchase a small fire place bellows for $10.00 to $15.00, or a sly look at one will show you how easy it is to make one. Plastic upholstery material can be the skin, and the body can be plywood. The valve is a scrap of the skin stapled loosly over the intake hole, and there is no exhaust valve.

A foot operated tire pump can be fit with a hose, and it is handy to use as you guide the hose with your hand as you pump air with your foot. There are some cheap hand and foot pumps that are made for inflatable mattresses and toys that will serve very well as a shop air supply.

HANDLING THE MOLTEN METAL

The metal is melted in a crucible or pot, and this is simple and easy as boiling water. It is more dangerous because of the higher temperature, but it is not difficult or highly technical. The real moment of danger is when you transfer the metal from the furnace to the mold, and that is why we are talking about handling it before we talk about melting it.

Crucibles are made of clay, clay and graphite or silicon carbide. These are all ceramic, and they are made in the same general way as pottery. They are also delicate, and they are quite costly. I consider them impractical for the beginning home shop because you are almost certain to loose the first two or three before you learn how to use them. Only silicon carbide crucibles are durable enough for the novice, and the cost is generally prohibitive. It also requires more fuel to melt with them, and they can be easily broken when full of red hot molten metal. I do all of my melting now with iron or steel pots.

The only argument for using ceramic pots is when the metal must be absolutely pure. In commercial practice the iron or steel pots for melting aluminum are coated with a refractory wash or lining to prevent the melt from picking up iron from the pot. I use my pots without a wash, and

I find no fault in my castings that I could attribute to
iron pick up. It's probably there, but it causes no problem that I can detect in my work.

A plumber's lead pot is ideal for melting aluminum or
pot metal. A 25 Pound pot measures about 6" in diameter
and about 4" deep. It will melt a bit more than one quart,
or about 5 pounds of aluminum. That's just enough for the
largest castings in these projects. You can make a similar
pot by welding a disc to a 5" length of 5" steel pipe. I
have one, made for me by a friend with a welder, that is of
extra heavy 4" pipe with a heavy disc welded to the bottom
that I have used for melting brass. Remember that it takes
a quantity of fuel to heat up the pot, so 1/8" wall thickness is sufficient for strength and durability. A heavy
pot will waste fuel and take much longer for the melt. A
cast iron one quart sauce pan with the handle cut off will
be durable for 40 or 50 melts, and a stainless steel sauce
pan will give you a few melts. I have used a one pound
coffee can for one melt only, but it is not durable, and it
is dangerous to handle molten metal in such a flimsy pot.
The pot must be strong enough to withstand handling when it
is red hot, and a light pot can only hold a small amount of
metal. A malleable iron pipe cap can be screwed to a short
pipe nipple to make a very serviceable pot.

Crucibles are sized by number, and the number represents the approximate capacity in pounds of aluminum. A
number 6 crucible is about 6 1/2" tall and 5 1/4" in diameter. It will hold about 6 pounds of aluminum or 18 pounds
of red brass. If you decide to use a ceramic crucible you
should choose a silicon carbide in a number 6 or smaller.

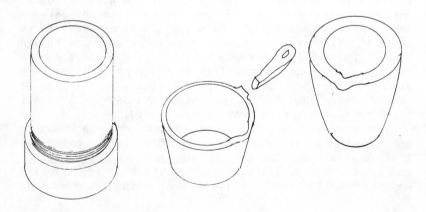

THE TONGS

The tongs for handling the pot of molten metal must be very strong and fit well so that there is no danger of any accident as you transfer the pot from the furnace to the mold.

If you use a ceramic pot, all professionals will advise you to purchase tongs to fit them rather than to make your own. A red hot pot full of molten metal is delicate, and pressure at the rim, or unequal pressure at any point, can burst the pot and dump the melt on your feet.

You can make a pair of tongs to handle an iron pot as shown below. Mine are made of 1/2" conduit in the same shape and size, but 1/2" steel rod is much stronger. Use steel or iron rivets to join the parts, rather than bolts and nuts. The bands that grip the pot can be 1/8" X 1" steel, and the curve should fit the pot very closely. You can make the tongs to grip an iron or steel pot at one side of the rim, but don't try to handle a ceramic pot by the rim.

The charcoal furnace makes an excellent forge to heat the steel for bending and flattening. You might make up a poker and skimmer at the same time, and your blacksmith work will be done.

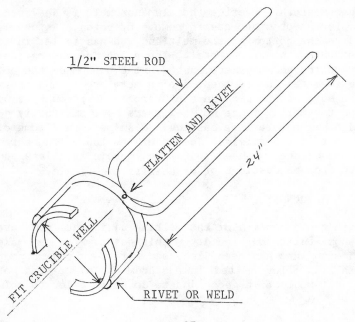

1/2" STEEL ROD

FLATTEN AND RIVET

24"

FIT CRUCIBLE WELL

RIVET OR WELD

27

FOUNDRY FLUX

There is a great deal about foundry work that has not been mentioned in this manual. An entire volume could be written about each subheading, but I have confined the text to those things I have experienced in developing a simple means to produce castings for the machinery projects. You can produce castings of high quality in aluminum and pot metal without flux in the melt, and I advise you to avoid using it until you have advanced to a higher level.

When metal is melted a portion of it will oxidize and the oxide and other impurities will precipitate in the melt. Flux is used to separate the impurity from the metal and float it to the top where it can be skimmed off. There are a wide variety of fluxes available for nearly every metal, but if you can buy a small quantity from a supply house you are lucky indeed. I've used a number of substitutes that have given more trouble than benefits, and the worst problem is that they eat up the pots rapidly.

Some fluxes act to combine with the impurities to form a slag to be skimmed away, and others act as a cover on the surface of the melt to prevent oxidation and gas pick up. In the charcoal foundry the melt will be covered with ash from the fire, and this seems to be an effective cover to protect the melt.

In commercial practice the aluminum melt is de-gassed with chlorine or other gas to remove hydrogen. A tube is pushed to the bottom of the melt and the gas is let in to bubble through the molten metal. There are de-gassers that are granular, and they are pushed to the bottom of the pot with an inverted cup on the end of a metal rod, and these release some gas to pick up the hydrogen as it bubbles up through the melt. I use no de-gassers now, and rarely do I find a gas bubble in a casting. I suspect that some of the effect of the original de-gasser remains in the scrap metal, and I see no need to try to improve it unless you need to produce castings of especially high grade.

YOU HAVE A FOUNDRY

With the exception of the melting equipment, you have just about built your foundry at this point. You can make a mold with what has been discussed so far, and you can pour it with zink alloy melted in a sturdy pan over a gas hot plate. It would be a good idea to do so in order to gain some experience in molding before you move on to the higher temperature that is required to melt aluminum or brass.

MAKESHIFT AND MAKE-DO

The improvisations and substitutes that are offered in these manuals are not intended to match their commercially made counterpart. If you can find commercially made foundry supplies and equipment, and can afford them, by all means use them. There is no doubt that they are superior and a desireable help. Even so, cost and availability are factors that most of us must face, and the substitute is the only answer sometimes, at least temporarily.

All of the modern equipment and machinery that is in common use today had its origin in just such rude and unrefined gadgetry as you are likely to devise as you begin to build your shop. There is no crime in evaluating a good thing and making an attempt to improve or simplify it. I don't advocate stealing another mans idea to take a free ride, but look at what others are doing and try to do it in a better, cheaper or simpler way. That is the theme of all inventive activity, and that is what needs to be revived in this age.

In case you are hesitant to begin in a metal working activity because you lack equipment or knowledge, remember that you will acquire skill and knowledge as you build the equipment, and neither is worth anything without the other. You may not know how to make a mold, but you can pound sand into a box, and that's the essence of it. You must risk a failure before you can succeed, so just start where you are and begin to build on it.

Much of what we will do will be makeshift and make-do. I planned the project to be done with little cash because I had little cash to spare for the purpose. As it progressed my shop grew, and I felt no pain in the pocketbook. Of more value than any piece of equipment, was the skill and knowledge I gained along the way.

Before we get into building the charcoal fired blast furnace, which is probably why you bought this book, we'll talk about making patterns and cores. Later, after we've built the melting equipment, we'll make some somple castings and put all of this to use enjoyably.

29

CHAPTER III

MAKING PATTERNS AND CORES

FIRST YOU NEED A PATTERN

The molten metal poured into a mold cavity makes a casting, and to make the mold you need a pattern. The pattern will be the size and shape of the desired casting, plus an allowance for shrinkage and machining. Fundamentally, if you can ram it into the sand and remove it to leave a clean cavity, you can use it for a pattern.

In a commercial shop a pattern is never made unless it is to be used for many castings, or someone is willing to pay the cost for one only, or a short run. We have much liberty in the home shop that could not be allowed in commercial operations because the patterns don't have to last as long. It is certain that the appearance of the casting will be no better than that of the pattern, so you will be called upon to exercise a measure of care and skill in some of your pattern making. Other items, though, you will simply whittle out of wood, plastic, wax or whatever is handy, cast it once, and throw the pattern away. You can even use a broken part that has been temporarily mended to make a mold to cast an exact replacement.

PATTERN MAKING EQUIPMENT

Most of your patterns will be made of wood, and ordinary hand wood working tools are all you really need. Power tools can be a great help in speeding up the work, but if your work area is small, and you don't work in wood for any other purpose, there is surely no need to buy or build a set of wood working power tools just for pattern making. If you have a sturdy work bench with a good vise, a few good quality hand wood working tools and a little patience you can get the job done. There will be much hole drilling in these projects, and a 3/8" electric hand drill is the one power tool that I would say is vital. It can be mounted on a stand on the bench to drive a sanding disc, grinding wheel, or even to serve as an improvised lathe to form some circular patterns. There are also some rotary rasps and shaping cutters, and accessories like a drum sander, that can be a great help at little cost.

A SANDING MACHINE

In the first edition of this manual I called this item a horizontal disc grinder. I had some very coarse open coated grinding discs that worked well for grinding aluminum castings, but they had no name or specification. I have not been able to find a replacement for them, and no disc that I can find works very well for grinding aluminum. It is very effective for wood sanding though, and it does a great job of sharpening a plane iron or a wood chisel if you use a disc of fine emery or silicon carbide grit. I think it would be more effective for pattern making if the disc was mounted vertically instead of horizontal.

The frame is of 1/8" X 1 1/2" angle iron, and it can be either bolted or welded together. The braces in the sides and the shelf are plywood, and the table can be either plywood or hard-board. Note that the angle iron feet are extended to counter balance the motor. If it is to be made a vertical model you can add a pair of angle iron brackets to support a shelf for the motor so that the arbor is just below the table. The table can be hinged at the back so that it can be raised for angular edge sanding or set at exactly 90 degrees.

A 1/4 or 1/3 horse power split phase motor will drive an 8" or 10" disc. A 3450 RPM motor is best, but a 1725 RPM motor will work very well. You can mount a threaded adapter arbor to the motor shaft and fit it with a disc of plywood to make a wheel. Once mounted you can use it like a face plate lathe to true up the face and edge with a very sharp wood chisel.

Both the abrasive discs and the cement used to fasten them to the wheel can be bought at most hardware departments, or you can cut the discs from the best abrasive paper or cloth that you can find.

Mount the switch in a metal box and use three wire cord with the ground wire connected to both the motor and the angle iron frame.

As with all power tools, work safe. Use eye protection when grinding, and be very wary of getting fingers or clothing caught on the wheel.

I used my horizontal sander throughout the entire series, and then modified it to make a sturdy bench for the lathe when I no longer needed it. It proved to be my most useful shop tool in the early stages of construction.

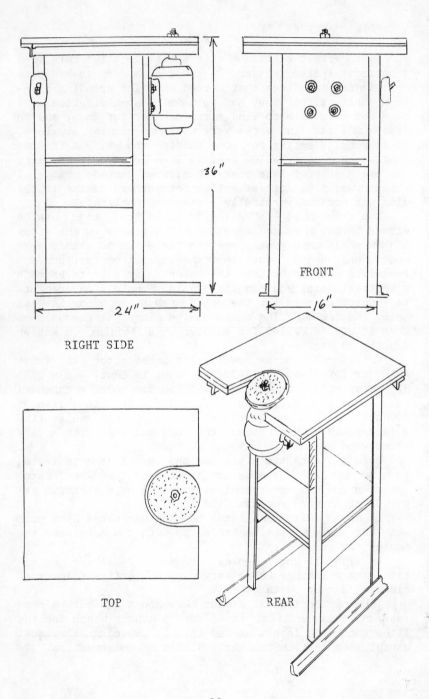

RIGHT SIDE

FRONT

36"

24"

16"

TOP

REAR

32

PATTERN DESIGN CONSIDERATIONS

The best way to evaluate a pattern problem is to begin with the shape you want to end up with and modify it to allow for the changes that will take place in the molding and casting process.

The most important design considerations are draft, shrinkage allowance, machining allowance, uniformity of section thickness and simplicity. We'll discuss each element of design and construction separately.

DRAFT AND PARTING

It is not enough to be able to ram the pattern into the sand, you must also be able to withdraw it to leave a clean mold cavity into which to pour the molten metal. For this reason sand molds are made in two or more parts, and the plane of division is called the parting. The pattern will be given slightly sloping sides, so that it can be easily drawn, and this is called the draft.

Some simple shapes will have a broad, flat side which is layed on the molding board, and the entire cavity will be in either the cope or the drag. More complex shapes require a pattern of two or more parts, and these are called split patterns. A portion of the cavity will be in the drag and the remainder will be in the cope. A cone or half ball is layed on its flat side and rammed into the sand, and it is easy to draw from the mold because it has positive draft from the parting line, which is its base. If you stood a straight sided cylinder on end and rammed it up it would be difficult to draw without damaging the cavity. If the end that is deepest in the mold were just slightly smaller than the base it would be easy to draw. If you layed the cylinder on its side and rammed it up you would have to dig it out of the sand, but you could split it along its center and ram half in the cope and the other half in the drag, and both halves would draw easily.

The object of draft is to make the deepest part of the pattern just a tiny bit smaller than its base size at the parting plane, and patterns are parted at the most convenient plane for easy molding and drawing.

A taper of 1/4" per foot, which is about 1 degree, is adequate for most patterns. Some applications, such as a hole in the pattern that will leave a core in the mold are given more draft for easy drawing.

SHRINKAGE AND MACHINING ALLOWANCE

The metal that is poured into the mold will shrink as it solidifies, and it will shrink more as it cools to room temperature. This shrinkage must be allowed for by increasing the size of the pattern in many cases, or the resulting casting won't fit its purpose. In other cases it will not be important.

A shrinkage allowance of 1/4" per foot will take care of the problem in casting aluminum and pot metal. Machining allowance will depend on the operations that must be done, but 1/16" to 1/8" will be adequate in most cases.

Pattern makers use a shrink rule for laying out dimensions on patterns. For our purpose a rule 12 1/4" long represents 12". The entire scale of the rule is expanded in proportion. If you layed out a 3" cube with the shrink rule it would measure 3 1/16" on all sides with a standard rule.

You can make one of stiff poster card by raising perpendicular lines from the scale divisions of a standard rule as seen below. You need divide only the first inch into sixteenths to make the job less tedious. You can varnish the finished rule for durability. Though it won't be a precision instrument, it will serve well enough for most of the work you will encounter in the home shop. It will not be required at all in this series of machine projects.

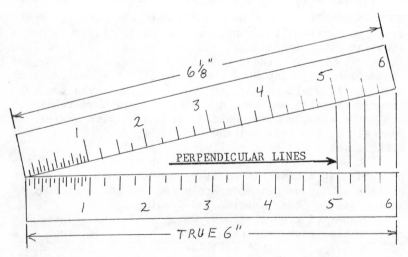

34

UNIFORMITY OF SECTION THICKNESS

Drastic changes in thickness and weight of sections must be avoided whenever possible. A uniform casting will solidify and cool at an equal rate all over for a sound casting. Heavy sections will solidify later than light ones, and they will give up some of their metal to the lightest parts to leave what is called a shrink cavity. If cooling is not equal there may be strains set up in the casting, and it may fail when put to use.

Feed risers are used to provide extra metal to heavy sections when they can't be avoided, and changes in weight of sections is done as gradually as possible.

Sharp corners must be avoided, so all corners are rounded or filleted except at the parting plane.

SIMPLICITY

It's always a temptation to " gussy " up a casting and include more in it than is really needed. In many cases it would be better to make two castings and bolt them together than to make a complicated casting in one piece. If you give a bit of time to the study of a pattern problem, it will take less time in molding, casting and finishing. Use what you have in material and means, and strive for simplicity. As you get involved the activity will instruct you, and you will quickly see your capabilities and limitations. A split pattern is very often easier to make and mold than a one piece pattern. Envision the shape through the entire process of pattern making, molding, casting and machining, and you will have little trouble with design.

CORES AND CORE PRINTS

Some castings will have hollow portions, and to do this you need a core. A core that is left in the mold by the pattern is called a green sand core. The bore for a pulley or a face plate is an example. It is sometimes necessary to push nails or wire through the core and into the main body of the mold so that the core won't be moved as the molten metal enters the cavity.

With more complex castings it may be necessary to ram up a green sand core separately and set it in the mold. A tricky business, but not so difficult if you prepare the core mold so that you can set it in the mold cavity and rap it to leave the core in the cavity as you lift out the core mold. Green sand doesn't lend itself too well to moving about without crumbling up. In either case, the sand of the core must not be rammed any harder than the sand of the main body of the mold. It will be surrounded by molten metal, and the sand must be porous enough to relieve the pressure of the gas, and to compress as the casting shrinks upon solidification and cooling.

A better way, when it is necessary to prepare a separate core, is to bake it. A baked core is made in a mold, which is called a core box, and it is baked in an oven to a dark brown color to drive out all moisture. If the core is not completely dry the steam will likely drive the metal out of the sprue and spoil the casting. It is also possible for a mold to blow up due to a wet core, and this is very dangerous.

The baked cores are located in the mold with prints to be left by extensions on the pattern, and they are called core prints.

There are many formulas for core mix. I use 20 parts of clean silica sand, 1 part wheat flour and molasses water. Molasses water is made of 10 parts water with 1 part molasses. Mix the sand and flour thoroughly while dry, temper with the molasses water, just as you do molding sand, and tamp it into the molding box. The box is dusted with talc or parting compound so that the core will release easily.

Cores must be vented to provide an easy path for steam and gas to escape. A vent wire can be pushed through if the core is large enough, or you can bed the wire in the core as you make it up, and then pull it out to leave the vent. Long slender cores are reinforced by bedding wire in them as they are made up.

There are other binders for core mix, like resin or linseed oil, but these just might get you in trouble with the wife when you bake them. Molasses and flour smells kind of nice when you bake it, and we need to stay in good grace if we hope to use the kitchen oven for baking cores.

Observe the same rules in core making that you do for pattern making. That is: draft, parting and simplicity. Try to design your castings so that they are not needed if it is at all possible. They add much labor and trouble to the job, and there is an extra measure of danger.

Green sand cores can be baked to make them more durable to handle, and in some cases that is the best answer. They won't be as strong, but they are easier to make.

A core box is generally a two part mold, but simple cylindrical shapes can sometimes be tamped into a tube and pushed out onto the core plate for baking.

There is only one casting in the entire series that is made with a baked core, and that is the tail stock for the lathe. The core is made in a box like that shown below, and it is rolled onto a metal plate to be baked.

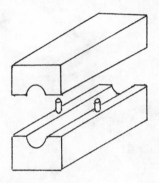

OTHER METHODS OF MOLDING

Green sand is not the only medium for molding. There is dry sand molding, lost wax investment casting, die casting, ceramic shell molding, and a host of methods that use chemical binders and special curing processes. All have their applications for specific purpose, but the technology is likely to be a bit discouraging to the novice. Green sand molding is easily learned, and initial expense is very low. You can turn out castings of remarkable accuracy and durability at very low cost, and you are building a foundation for growth in other directions if you choose.

There is a large, unfilled market for castings in all classifications. You are likely to find yourself in considerable demand once you get started. The equipment and methods that are described here are not suitable for any large output of castings, but you could produce single items or very small lots at a profit if you are careful to pass on the cost of all that is involved.

" The Metal Casters Bible ", Tab Book #1173, offers a very full discussion on most of what is known about all of the various methods of molding and casting. " The complete Handbook Of Sand Casting ", Tab Book #1043, and " Lost Wax Investment Casting ", Tab Book #725, will provide a thorough reference library at very moderate cost.

CHAPTER IV

THE BLAST FURNACE

The little furnace that is described in these pages is capable of turning out a surprising amount of molten metal at low cost. I call it a charcoal fired furnace only because other types of fuel are difficult to get in some localities, but you can get charcoal where ever you live. If you can get coal or coke you can use them, but charcoal is the most convenient choice. Coke is harder to ignite, and coal is very smoky and nasty until the volatile matter has been burned out.

Of course you can make a larger furnace. The five gallon pail is about as small as is practical for a solid fuel furnace, and a twenty gallon drum is about as large as one man can manage safely. It is no problem to melt a larger quantity of metal, but the surprise comes at the moment you need to get the pot out of the furnace and transfer it to the mold. An immense amount of heat is radiated by the pot, and there is no time to think it over at that moment. I urge you to start small, and move on to greater things when you have mastered the art on a small scale.

This unit, with a one quart pot, will give a full melt of aluminum in a very short time. I manage it in about 20 minutes from a cold start, and subsequent melts are a bit faster. Reports from readers who have built the furnace range from 10 minutes to 30 minutes, and the main differences are in the air supply and the weight of the pot. If your pot is of extra heavy metal it will take more fuel and time to get a melt, and the regulation of the air supply will greatly effect the melting time and fuel consumption.

CAUTION

Charocal, coal and coke are essentially carbon. when burned at high temperatures they produce carbon monoxide in dangerously high quantities. Carbon monoxide is odorless, colorless, tasteless and DEADLY POISON. Use your furnace outside, and dump the fuel charge before you bring it into an occupied area for storage between use.

If you have a well ventilated work area, and want to be able to melt indoors, you should consider a small gas fired melting unit. such a unit can be purchased from Pyramid Products, 3736 South 7th Ave., Phoenix AZ 85401. This is practical home foundry equipment at reasonable cost, and they also have some of the materials and supplies you will need. Send them $1.00 for a listing of what is available.

BUILDING THE FURNACE

This is simple work, very much like working with concrete or mortar. It is likely that you have much of what is needed on hand, and the remainder won't be hard to get. A clean 5 gallon metal pail, a piece of sheet metal about 18" X 30", some scraps of plywood, some wire and a roll of tape make up the body and form. Sand and fire clay are all you need for the lining, or you can purchase a castable refractory mix for the lining. Add an old vacuum cleaner or a hair dryer, a bag of charcoal and a pot for the metal and you are ready to go to work.

Construction is even easier than I first believed, for it took me three days to build my first furnace. I've built another for the preparation of this revision, and it only took three hours, I didn't make a new lid for the second furnace though, so that accounts for some of the time, but the whole process requires little work and time. The first furnace has endured for three years and it is still good.

The 5 gallon pail is the main body of the furnace, and its handle is left on to move the furnace about. The air blast inlet is called the tuyere (tweer), and it's just a hole near the bottom of the furnace. The common hair dryer hose is about 1 1/4" in diameter, so locate a hole 2" form the bottom of the pail for the tuyere. A short length of 1 1/4" thin wall tubing can be split and expanded so that another piece of 1 1/4" tubing can slip in easily, and this will provide the form for the tuyere. The inside form is centered in the pail with wooden strips and the re-fractory lining is packed in around the form. The strips are raised as the refractory is packed in, and when the walls are complete the form is removed, and the bottom of the lining is packed in level with the bottom of the tuyere.

THE INSIDE FORM

A cylinder of 7" to 8" in diameter is what is needed, and unless you can collapse it you will have a hard time getting it out after you have packed in the lining.

Galvanized sheet metal of 28 or 30 gauge is heavy enough for the form. A pair of plywood discs will form the ends, and you can fasten it together with nylon reinforced tape or duct tape. The bottom disc is solid and the top has a hand grip so that it can be pulled out easily. A screw is driven into the bottom disc to provide a grip for pulling it out when the form is removed.

Cut the discs from 3/4" plywood and cut a saw slot in the edge of each one about 1" deep.

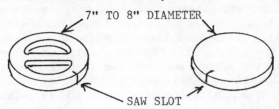

7" TO 8" DIAMETER

SAW SLOT

Hook a tape measure in the saw slot and measure around the circumfrence of the disc to find the length of the sheet metal form, and measure the inside height of the pail to find the height of the form. Add 2" to the length and cut the sheet metal to these dimensions. Bend up a 1" flange at one end of the form.

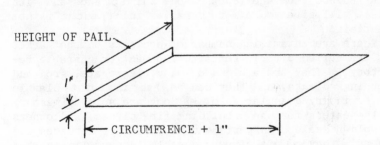

HEIGHT OF PAIL

1"

CIRCUMFRENCE + 1"

Locate a disc on each end, with the slot slipped over the flange, and fasten it with a strip of tape. Roll it up and fasten the overlap with three or four strips of tape.

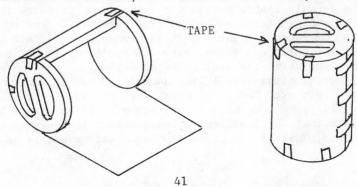

TAPE

41

Foundry ceramics is a subject so broad and complex that a large volume is required just to discuss the fundamental principles. There is no need to know that much about it because we are only going to build one little furnace.

The refractoriness of a substance is its ability to withstand the punishment of high temperature without being destroyed. Silica sand and clay are two substances that will do the job. Clay becomes plastic in nature when it is mixed with water, and when the mixture is heated to high temperature it is vitrified, or fused, into a solid mass. It will not again become plastic when it is moistened, and it will stand high temperatures for a long period of time.

If you made the furnace lining of nothing but clay it would crack and crumble before you had it cured. Primitive potters learned that if they added bits of broken pottery to their clay it would be less likely to shrink and crack when it was fired. The modern ceramist calls this grog. You can purchase grog from a dealer in pottery supplies, or you can make it by smashing up some scraps of fire brick. If you replace from one fourth to one third of the sand with grog it will give you a more durable lining, but it is not essential.

There are an amazing number of products on the market that are called plastic refractory cement or castable refractory. They are a blend of clay, aggregate, grog and other ingredients, and they can be had in moist plastic form or in dry granular form. Some are sold by masonry supply dealers for use in building fire places, and others are sold by dealers in parts and supplies for furnaces and boilers. They will make a very durable furnace lining, but they are quite expensive. If cost is important to you, the simple formula presented here is cheap and durable.

Two parts of silica sand mixed with one part fire clay is the formula that was used for many years to patch the linings of blast furnaces and to line ladles. I used grog in the mix when I built the first furnace, but I left it out when I built the second one. I can't say that I see any difference in the linings after firing.

These quantities will line the furnace and lid, and some will be left over for later repairs if needed. It will keep well for a long time if you store it in an air tight container. Mix 5 gallons of sand with 2 1/2 gallons of fire clay, just as you would mix sand and cement to make mortar or concrete. You can mix in an old tub or on the floor, or in a mortar box as seen in the photo below. A garden hoe works very well, or you can use a large trowel.

When it is thoroughly mixed you can begin to add water very sparingly. A garden type sprinkling can or a fine mist from the hose is ideal. Avoid making pools in the mix because it will separate the ingredients. Wet the mix only as fast as it will absorb water, and mix thoroughly each time you add water. Keep the texture as uniform as possible throughout the mixing. Continue until the entire mass is about the consistency of very stiff mortar. Only two to three quarts of water will be used, and the mix is only slightly more moist than tempered molding sand. Too much water lengthens the curing time, causes excess shrinking and weakens the lining. Test it as you would molding sand, by squeezing a handful into a ball and breaking it in half. The final step is easy, just cover it with a sheet of plastic or a wet cloth so it won't dry out, and let it stand until tomorrow. It will do no harm to let it stand for any length of time, just so you don't let it dry out. It may even improve the quality to let it cure for a week or more before you use it to line the furnace.

The inside form is rested on the bottom of the pail and centered with 4 wooden strips, as seen in the photo on the previous page. the object is to pack in the mix to uniform density, with no voids, to form the wall of the furnace. Put the mix in about 2" layers, and ram down each layer with a stick before you add more. Raise the strips as you progress, and work in a spiral pattern. Ram at an angle to be sure that the area below the strips is filled as you raise them. When the lower level is filled to the bottom of the tuyere, you can put in the tuyere form with a tube inside it to hold it in place. fill the entire form as seen in the photo below.

Tamp the mix in firmly, but be careful not to displace or deform the inside form. Once you have reached the half way point the strips can probably be taken out, but don't let the inside form be driven off center. When you have reached the top you can smooth it up with a trowel.

Now you can peel back the tape that holds the top disc in place and pull out the disc. Drive a screw into the bottom disc and grip it with a pliers to pull it out at an

angle.   Grip the flange of the sheet metal form and turn
it as you lift it out.   Rough up the wall at the bottom,
and proceed to ram in the bottom lining until it is even
with the bottom of the tuyere hole.

Check the lining all over carefully, and if there are
any voids fill them with refractory mix.
the main body of the furnace is now ready to cure.   It
must be kept covered with plastic or wet cloth until it is
fired to avoid spalling.   Spalling means that if you let the
skin dry out there will be trapped water in the lining.   As
you heat it the water will turn to steam and blow chunks of
the lining off.   You can fire it immediately, or wait as
long as you wish, so long as it is kept moist.

THE LID FORM

The lid is rammed up with the same mix, but because it
must be moved about it is reinforced with a wire grid.   The
form is a sheet metal band which remains as the outside rim
of the finished lid.
Measure around the circumfrence of the furnace body to
find the length of the lid form.   Add 1" to the dimension

and lay it off on a strip of sheet metal 2" wide. Divide
the length of the form into 12 equal spaces, and drill or
punch a 1/8" hole in the center of the strip at each division. Add a pair of holes 1/2" from each end, so that you
can form it into a hoop and fasten with screws or rivets.

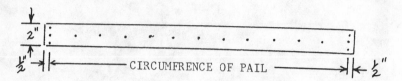

Make a template of heavy cardboard to hold the rim in
shape while you weave a cross pattern of wires through the
1/8" holes. The rim should fit the template snugly so it
won't be pulled our of round by the wire grid.
Add a pair of ears made of 1/8" strap iron, and make a
pair of heavy wire hooks or rings to fit the ears. You
can fashion a pair of heavy handles if you prefer. These
are for lifting the lid from the hot furnace.

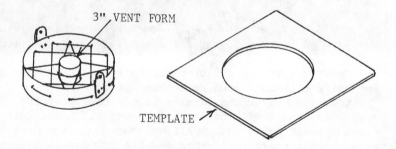

The 3" vent hole goes in the center of the lid. I was
able to find a water glass that was just about right. You
will have to use double wires in the center holes so that
a wire will pass on each side of the vent form.

RAMMING UP THE LID

Place the rim in the cardboard template and center the
vent form with the wire grid. Tamp the form full of the
same refractory mix you used for the furnace and smooth up
the top surface with a trowel. Cover it until it is cured.

CURING THE REFRACTORY LINING

The curing is done gradually. Moderate heat is used first to drive out the water, and then the temperature is raised rapidly to fuse the lining into one piece.

the lid is needed in the final firing of the furnace, so it must be cured first. You can lay it on a piece of sheet metal and bake it in the kitchen oven at 250 degrees until it stops steaming, (about 2 or 3 hours), then raise the temperature to 350 to 400 degrees for 5 or 6 hours. It won't make nasty smells in the kitchen, so your wife won't mind. Later you can take her out to dinner. You've saved enough money building your own blast furnace so that you can afford it.

There will be some shrinkage as the lid cures, and one or more cracks may develop. Just moisten them and pack in some of the left over refractory mix and continue to bake. It will be best to allow the lid to cool slowly in the oven rather than to expose it to cool air immediately.

I cured the lining of my first furnace with a wood fire to drive out the steam, and then I ran up a hot fire with charcoal and the air blast to vitrify it. This took all night for the wood fire, and considerable time to feed it until I had the entire furnace full of glowing coals. On the second furnace I simply built a charcoal fire and let it burn without the blast until all of it was ignited. I put on the lid and turned on the air blast after about one hour, and ran the blast until most of the fuel was consumed. Then I covered the vent and the tuyere with bricks and let lt cool slowly. The lining appears to be as good, if not better than the first one, and it took much less time.

Needless to say, the firing of the main body must be done outside. There will be showers of sparks from the vent, so make sure you are far enough away from anything that could catch fire. Be wary of catching a sleeve or a pants leg on fire.

Lay a double layer of charcoal in the bottom of the furnace and soak it with starting fluid. Carry the can of starting fluid at least 10 feet away before you light the fire. Allow the first double layer to ignite well before you add another double layer. When the furnace is about two thirds full, and well ignited, you can put on the lid and start the air blast. Steam will rise from the lining for some time, and then it will gradually raise to a red heat. Remove the air tube and cover the vent and tuyere with any

47

kind of bricks, and allow it to cool slowly for three or four hours.

If any cracks form in the lining you can moisten them and pack in some of the left over mix to repair them.

THE AIR BLAST

It does not require very much air to run such a small fire up to a high heat. A husky hair dryer is adequate for melting aluminum or pot metal, and you can connect it with the dryer's flexible hose slipped over a length of thin wall tubing to fit the tuyere, as seen in the photo on page 38.

If you melt brass in small quantities you will need a more powerful blower, and a vacuum cleaner will do the job. You must add a shutter to the air inlet, or a blast gate in the discharge to regulate the volume of air. Too much air will make the fire act like a cutting torch, and it will quickly burn the bottom out of your pot. This was the problem most often encountered with the use of large blowers.

The blast tube is meant to slip easily into the tuyere so that it can be removed when the blast is shut down. The heat will travel down the tube and melt the hose if it is left in place without air blowing through it.

It's a good idea to provide a safety hole in the bottom of the air tube at about mid way. Make it about 1/2" in diameter, and cover it with a piece of paper or a thin sheet of lead or tin. This will protect the hose and the blower in case a pot spills and molten metal runs down the tube.

MELTING IN THE CHARCOAL FURNACE

As mentioned earlier, the charcoal fired furnace will generate carbon monoxide in dangerous quantity. It is not safe to operate it indoors.

There will be occasional showers of sparks from the vent, and the exhaust gas is very hot. Operate the furnace well away from buildings or anything flammable. Hot gas leaking around the lid may not be visible, but it can ignite your clothing or anything near by that is flammable.

It is extremely dangerous to spill molten metal on any damp surface, especially concrete or stone. Prepare a sand bed about 2" thick and about 3 or 4 feet square, and don't carry a pot of metal outside the bed area. Damp concrete or stone will explode and shower the area with molten metal and bits of hot rock.

48

Before you melt any metal, provide a place to get rid of all that you plan to melt. You will have excess metal with each melt, and if a mold runs out at the parting you may have to dump the entire charge. It must not be allowed to solidify in the pot, because the pot may break when you attempt to reheat it to melt it. I use an old biscuit tin for aluminum and pot metal, and it divides the left over metal into handy sized ingots for future use. You can also press a series of dents into the bed sand to form small ingot molds for the excess metal. A single blob will be very difficult to break up into useable pieces.

Work safely. Wear glasses when you look into the vent hole. don't wear highly flammable clothing. Wear good leather shoes, not sneakers or sandals. You are certain to step on hot metal or spill a dab, and your feet are in great danger. Make sure that you have an absolutely firm grip on the pot, and that you can set it down safely before you pick it up. Clear the area of anything that might trip you as you carry the pot, and never walk backwards. Plan your work so that you can move forward in a circle to pour your molds, and return the pot safely to the furnace.

Just one more word of caution before we fire up. The fire is started with charcoal starting fluid. This innocent looking stuff injures or kills someone all too often. It gets spilled on the clothing, making a torch of you if it ignites, and panic follows. Most dangerous of all, is trying to squirt a bit more on a fire that is not going well enough to suit you. The fire follows the stream back into the can and it explodes, showering all near by with burning fluid. Death is sometimes the result, and the picnic is surely ruined. Read the safety directions on the can and follow them. I make certain to carry my can of fluid at least 10 feet away before I take a match in hand.

You can make an effective starting fluid by adding one quart of gasoline to two gallons of kerosene or fuel oil. The mixture ignites with a bit of a puff, so drop the match into it rather than getting too close with the hands. An ounce or two is enough to start a fire.

LIGHTING UP

Place a double layer of charcoal in the bottom of the furnace, soak it with lighting fluid and ignite it. Don't forget to carry your fluid a safe distance away before you light the fire. When the initial fuel charge is burning nicely you can add more charcoal until there is just enough room left for the pot, and a bit of clearance at the top. Set the pot on the coals and, if there is room for it, add more charcoal around the sides of the pot.

Drop scraps of aluminum into the pot and fill it to the top. don't pack or wedge the scrap, or the pot may break as the metal expands from the heat.

Set the lid on the furnace and slip the air tube into the tuyere opening and turn on the air blast.

ADJUSTING THE AIR VOLUME

If you are using a small hair dryer for a blower you will probably not have to adjust the air volume at all, but a larger blower will deliver too much air at full volume.

The ideal fire for melting metal is just a little bit short of enough air for perfect combustion. This is called a reducing fire because the free carbon is hungry for oxygen. It will actually steal oxygen from oxidized metal and reduce it to pure metal. This is one of the ways used to reduce metalic ores to metal.

If the fire is left too short of air it will be smoky and dirty, and temperatures will not get high enough for efficient melting.

An excess of air makes an oxidizing fire which is very hot, but the excess oxygen will burn up the melt, and probably burn the bottom out in the bargain. The high volume of air also carries the heat out the vent, and fuel is consumed to no purpose.

Begin with the shutter or gate closed, and very slowly open it while observing the flame. When you reach a point where opening the shutter a bit more does not effect flame quality, you have a slightly oxidizing fire. Close the shutter a small amount to give a reducing flame. the adjustment is not nearly as critical with solid fuel as it is with a gas fired unit.

Keep in mind that the volume of air will increase as fuel is consumed because resistance to the air flow is decreased. For long melts you must lift out the pot and add more fuel to keep the fuel bed height right.

POURING TEMPERATURE

Aluminum pours best at between 1350 and 1400 degrees fahrenheit. Most home shop operators can't justify the expense of a pyrometer, and it is not at all necessary for the class of work we will be doing in these projects.

The various shades of red heat will have little meaning to you until you have had some experience in observing the condition of the metal at a given color. Faintly showing red heat in a dark room would indicate about 950 degrees. The same showing in bright light could indicate 1200 or more degrees, so your error could be as much as 300 or 400 degrees. It will be best to judge the metal in terms of its fluidity, rather than to try to guess the temperature.

The metal will absorb heat as a solid, and its temperature will rise rapidly until it reaches the melting point. Then the temperature will remain constant while it continues to absorb heat as it changes from solid to liquid. At this point it is said to be saturated, and the idea is to add an additional amount of heat so that it will remain in the liquid state until it fills the mold. This is called super heating. You will learn to rely on more than one sensible factor by which you'll judge the temperature.

Excessive stirring of the melt must be avoided because it corrupts the metal, but a light stirring with a steel rod of about 1/4" diameter will give you a feel of its fluidity. If it is too cool it will congeal in a blob on the end of the rod, but it will slip off easily when hot enough. Observe the color at various conditions, and you will begin to train your eye.

The pot must be skimmed before pouring, and this is one more chance to judge its fluidity and observe the color. An amount of dross will form in the melt, and it will float on the top of the metal. In the case of exceptionally dirty metal it will form a sponge like mass. Much good metal is salvaged if you press the mass of dross against the side of the pot to wring it out. The impurities will then form a powder that is easily skimmed off. The charcoal and ash that settles on the melt will do no harm, and they provide an excellent cover to prevent the melt from picking up gas during the heat. A thin layer of dross on top is beneficial, and you just skim it to one side when you pour.

As the metal settles in the pot you can add more, but not so much that you freeze what has already melted. It is dangerous to handle a brim full pot, so you should limit yourself to a partially filled pot until you are very sure of what you are doing.

The pot will settle with the fuel bed, and you must be on watch to see that it doesn't tip and spill the melt.

Melting pot metal in the charcoal furnace is a little like rabbit hunting with an elephant gun. It requires only a temperature of 750 to 800 degrees fahrenheit to melt the stuff, and the furnace will reach that so quickly that you must use the air blast only enough to establish the heat. Once melted, the glowing coals will maintain temperature for a long time.

Pot metal contains a high percentage of zink, which is vaporized easily when over-heated. It alters the alloy and it is harmful to breath the vapors. It's more practical to melt pot metal on a gas hot plate, but you can do it with the charcoal furnace if you are careful.

Brass and bronze can be melted in small quantities in the charcoal furnace if you have an adequate air supply and a sturdy pot. Use a silicon carbide crucible, with tongs made especially to fit it, or an extra heavy steel pot that you might make up with extra heavy pipe with a disc welded to the bottom.

Contrary to popular belief, brass and bronze are not easy to work with. They pour at temperatures about 1000 degrees above that of aluminum, and there are fluxing problems along with the extra danger due to the higher temperatures. Master these simple techniques first, and you can move up to brass and iron in a few simple steps later on.

You can remove the pot to add more fuel, and you can melt continuously for a long time. The furnace will become choked up with ash and klinker though, and you will have to set the pot aside and dump out the fire. Use a tongs to put the live coals back in, and add fresh fuel to start a new cycle.

Keep a pair of bricks near the furnace, on which to set the lid when you remove it. Set the pot on the lid when you add fuel or pull out klinkers. Don't set either the pot or the lid on a cold or damp surface.

On occasion the pot will tilt to be impossible to get hold with the tongs. You can grasp it on the rim with a pair of long pliers, but you must wear very heavy protective gloves or mitts. Ordinary welders gloves don't protect the back of the hand, and your knuckles will be parbroiled before you can set the pot down. Heavy asbestos or non-bestos gloves are available at about $20.00 per pair from some of the sources that will be listed at the end of this book. There are also aprons and leggings available, so don't be without protection. Make sure you have what is needed to complete any move you begin before you start.

CHAPTER V

MOLDING AND POURING

in this chapter the idea is to give you some actual experience in casting that will instruct you in the use of your new equipment, prepare you to make the parts for the machines you want to build, and to produce some practical items that will become a permanent part of your shop. Your raw material is aluminum and die cast metal. It is surprising to see how much of the stuff is laying around waiting for you to pick it up once you begin to watch for it. Auto pistons, pots and pans, gear housings, extrusions, and countless items of aluminum scrap will quickly accumulate into a generous supply. Large scrap, like a transmission housing, can be heated over a large charcoal fire to make them easy to break up. Just make a ring of bricks and build the fire inside. Lay the large scrap on the fire and cover it with a tent of bricks. Use your blower to run up the draft. The temperature will rise to a point called " hot shortness ", when the metal will easily crumble up like a cooky into nut sized pieces. It requires only light blows of the hammer, while it would be nearly impossible to break up when cold, even with a sledge hammer.

Zink die casting metal is generally called pot metal. It is used to make thousands of items for automobiles, machines and appliances. It does not enjoy the reputation it deserves because it is generally used in die castings of very thin section. Some alloys, such as Zamak, are actually stronger than iron is some respects. it is one of the handiest materials you will find for home castings. Its salvage value is just about a penny a pound, so you can't hope to find a cheaper material. It's worth noting that much of what you buy in home workshop equipment is made of die castings with very thin sections. The material works very well in green sand molds, and there is no reason why we can't use it to make our own parts in heavier sections for greater strength and durability. It will be superior to aluminum for some items.

A SIMPLE CASTING

The simplest casting of all would be to melt a pot of metal and pour it into a depression in the bed sand. The result would be a non-descript blob of metal with no useful purpose.

This would be an open mold casting, and it is possible to produce some useful items in this way. A paper weight, a door stop, a book end; even some pretty complicated shapes where one surface can be left rough, or machinery is available to finish it. I've never wanted a book end, a paper weight or a door stop, so the only time I use an open mold is when I cast a supply of ingots for future use.

CLOSED MOLDS

Since it is assumed that you have no machine shop at the start of this project, it is important to have the castings as near to finished condition as possible when they are shaken from the sand. With good pattern design and careful molding practice it is possible to produce some of the castings to require no finishing at all. Others will require finishing steps that are kept to a minimum by careful planning of shape and dimension in the closed molding process.

Provided that the mold cavity is durable, and the metal is hot enough to remain fluid until the mold is filled, there is little that could go wrong in an open mold. While a closed mold gives better control over shape, dimension and texture, a different set of conditions exists in closed molds that must be taken into consideration.

Pressure in the mold cavity is of first importance. It is the hydro-static pressure of the molten metal that gives the desired accuracy in the closed mold. The pressure of the molten metal is exerted equally in all directions, and it is a function of the weight of the metal and the height of the column. It is sometimes a help to increase the depth of the mold or the height of the risers to raise the hydro-static pressure in the mold. A tin can with both ends cut out makes a convenient form to raise the height of the sprue and risers above the top of the cope on small molds.

The sand must be rammed firmly enough so that the pressure of the metal won't deform the cavity. On large molds the hydro static pressure can be great enough to lift the cope and let the metal run out at the parting. Such molds must be clamped together or weighted.

When the molten metal enters the cavity it will generate steam and gas as it raises the temperature of the water and other elements in the sand. This pressure is relieved

by the porosity of the sand and by venting with the wire.
If it were not relieved it would drive the metal back out
the sprue and spoil the casting. The sand must not be rammed so tightly as to prevent the escape of steam and gas.
A happy medium is found with a little practice, and generous use of the vent wire will prevent serious problems until you get the hang of it.

If a core is used in the mold, whether green sand or
baked, it must be strong enough to withstand the pressure
of the metal, porous enough to vent steam and gas and re-
sillient enough to collapse when the metal shrinks on cooling. Green sand cores are rammed no harder than the main
body of the mold, and baked cores are thoroughly dried to
avoid generating excess steam and gas.

FEEDING THE MOLD

A number of physical and chemical changes take place
when metal is melted. As the temperature of the solid is
raised it expands. If the temperature continues to rise
it will become a liquid at its specific melting point. It
continues to expand as the temperature rises, and it will
become a gas at a still higher temperature. While it is
at high temperature it is more active chemically, and will
combine more readily with elements in contact with it.

The same events occur in reverse as the metal cools.
It will shrink as it solidifies, and it will shrink more
as it cools to room temperature. Any compounds that were
formed by chemical action will be a part of the casting.

The metal must be heated enough to remain fluid until
the mold is filled, but not so hot as to cause excess chemical action, or, as in the case of zink based alloys, to
actually vaporize a part of the alloy and lose it in the
form of gas or oxide.

The casting process may well be compared with filling
the ice cube tray with water and placing it in the freezing compartment of the refrigerator. It will slowly lose
heat until the water begins to solidify, forming ice cubes,
which are really open mold castings.

Water differs in that it expands upon freezing, while
most metals will contract. (There are exceptions.) As
it changes from liquid to solid a thin skin of ice forms,
and, as freezing progresses towards the center, the cube is
deforemd by internal pressure due to the change of state.
If you freeze a container of water without providing room

for the expansion the container will burst at its weakest point.

If the water was let into the tray slowly through a small chilled tube it would be likely to freeze in the tube and the tray would be only partially filled. If it was warmed up a bit it may fill the mold, but it would turn to slush on contact with the chilled tray and imperfect cubes would result.

these are problems that actually occur in modern ice making equipment, and they also occur in metal casting. If the metal is allowed to enter the mold too cool or too slow it will solidify before the mold is filled.

The main difference is in that the metal will shrink upon solidification, rather than expand, and provision is made for the shrinkage. If sprues, risers and runners are too small they will solidify before the casting, and they will actually rob metal from the mold to leave a shrink cavity in the casting. Likewise, a light portion of a casting will solidify first and rob metal from adjoining heavy sections. If an actual cavity is not left, there will at least be a severe internal strain to weaken the casting.

Sprues and risers are made heavier than the sections they feed, and they are located to enter the mold at the heaviest parts of the mold to replace any metal robbed by lighter sections as they solidify. It is often necessary to add several feed risers to complex shapes. Large runners are sometimes used to provide plenty of molten metal to broad thin sections at several places so that a complex mold will be completely filled.

A critical examination of each pattern will be required to determine proper gating and feeding. A general rule is that the sprue or riser should be at least 50% larger than the section thickness of the part it feeds. When in doubt, go to the next larger size or add another riser.

YOU ARE ALMOST A SAND CRAB

You don't have to blacken your face and crawl backward through the sand, but you are ready to go to work now.

Choose anything that you feel capable of molding, and roll up your sleeves and go to work. I suggest something very simple for your first casting, but something that you will use in your shop. The core plates, a rapping bar, a face plate or sanding disc, or even some household item you might like to present to your wife.

56

CAST A PAIR OF CORE PLATES

Any simple shape that has at least one flat surface can be molded and casted by this same procedure. I offer the core plates as a first project because of the simplicity, and they will soon have practical value in projects that will follow.

Some commercially made core plates are cast in aluminum. They are heat treated to normalize them, and carefully machined for a true flat surface. The core requirements are not so exacting in the home shop. We need only a reasonably flat surface that can easily be accomplished with a large double cut file, a sheet of coarse abrasive or by hand scraping. It's a simple project that will give you a complete molding and casting experience.

MAKE THE PATTERNS

Two pieces of 1/4" plywood, each 3" X 6", and beveled all around the edge for draft, will provide the patterns. Fill any flaws in the edge grain and sand them smooth. A slightly rounded edge and corners makes for easy drawing from the mold, but leave the edges sharp at the parting plane. A slope of one degree or less is adequate for such a shallow pattern. Seal with two coats of lacquer or varnish. An aerosol can of fast drying lacquer is handy for sealing small patterns.

THE FLASK

A 12" X 12" flask, with each half 3 1/2" deep, will be just right for this job. It will be handy for many other molds in these projects as well. Prepare a molding board and a bottom board to suit the flask, and you are ready to make a mold.

TEMPER THE SAND

Squeeze a handful of sand to see if it is properly tempered. If it is too dry you can sprinkle on a little water and mix it up well. Shake it through the riddle and let it stand for a while before you test again. If it is too wet you can mix in some dry sand, or let a fan blow over it and mix it up from time to time. You want just enough moisture for good bond, but not enough to make a steam bomb.

Place the patterns on the molding board, parting face down, and dust a light film of parting over the entire surface. Just hold the dust bag about 12" above the board, and shake it as you move it around.

Invert the drag and place it on the molding board so that the patterns are somewhat centered. Riddle in an inch or so of sand, and tamp it down all around the patterns with your hands. This will bed the patterns and the drag so that they won't move around as you finish ramming. Add another inch or so of sand, and this time use the wedge shaped end of the rammer to peen the sand all around the patterns and towards the sides of the flask. Use the blunt end of the rammer to ram all over the surface of the sand. You want the sand to be more firmly packed around the edge of the flask and the patterns than you do directly over the patterns. The rule is: Firm enough to hold the shape of the pattern, but porous enough for free venting.

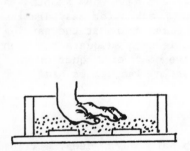
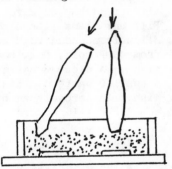

Now scoop the flask heaping full of sand. Peen all around the pattern and flask, and ram the entire surface of the sand with the blunt end of the rammer. When the drag is rammed mounded full you can strike off the surface level with the edge of a straight board.

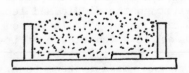
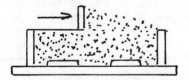

If the drag is not firm enough it will yield under the pressure of ramming the cope sand. The pattern may shift, or the metal may run out at the parting when you pour. If the sand is rammed too tightly the steam and gasses won't be able to escape and will drive the metal back out of the sprue. More complicated shapes require more attention to the ramming to ensure uniform density and proper hardness of the mold. Experience will quickly teach you how.

VENT THE DRAG

Run the vent wire into the mold, almost to the pattern, in about six places over each pattern. If you go all the way to the pattern you may cast some aluminum wire when you pour the mold. It is not a serious problem. They will be easy to break off when the casting is shaken out.

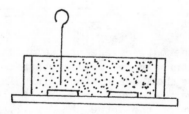

RUB IN THE BOTTOM BOARD

Sprinkle a handful of sand over the bottom of the drag and lay the bottom board over the loose sand. Rub the board in a back and forth circular motion until it rests firmly on the frame of the drag. This is called rubbing in the bottom board, and it is done to ensure firm, even support to the entire surface when the cope is rammed up.

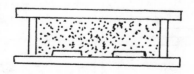

ROLL OVER THE DRAG

Grasp the entire group, like you would a giant sand-wich, and roll it over. The bottom board will now rest on the bench and you can remove the molding board. You will see the parting face of the pattern, imbedded in the drag sand.

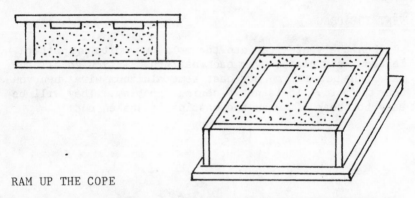

RAM UP THE COPE

Now dust the entire face of the drag with parting, as you did the patterns on the molding board. Set the cope in place, and press the sprue pin about 1/2" into the drag sand between the two patterns. A length of broom handle about 6" long will do for the sprue pin. Fill, ram and vent the cope, just as you did the drag. Be careful not to displace the pattern as you ram.

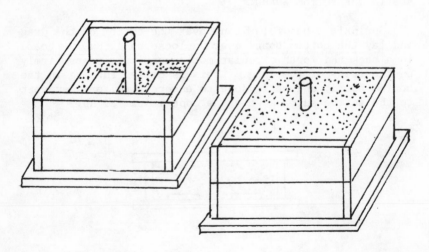

OPEN THE MOLD

Rap the sprue pin to loosen it and pull it straight up.
It will leave a hole in the cope and a print in the drag.
Lift the cope straight up and set it on edge behind the
drag. Blow away any loose sand with the bellows.
Swab all around the pattern to strengthen the bond at
the edge so it won't break when you draw the patterns.

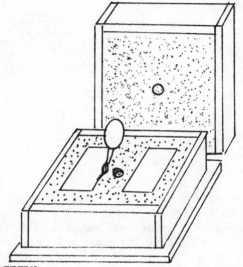

DRAW THE PATTERN

Turn a screw or a screw eye into the center of the pattern for a draw peg, and rap all around it with a metal rod
to loosen the pattern in the mold. The cavity will be en-
larged slightly, and you can lift the pattern straight up
without damaging the cavity.

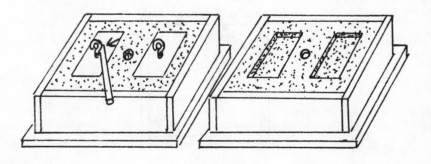

CUT THE GATE

Cut a channel about 1/2" wide and 1/4" deep from each cavity to the sprue print. Swab the gates and slick them up so that loose particles won't be washed into the mold. Round the corners of the gate with your fingers or a handy tool that suits the purpose.

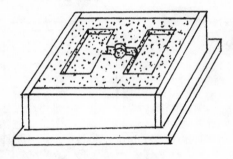

CLOSE THE MOLD

Cut or press the top of the sprue opening to a funnel shape and swab the bottom of the opening to round the edge.

Blow through the sprue opening with the bellows, and also blow off the face of the cope and drag. Any loose particles in the cavity can be removed by spitting on the end of a stick and lifting them out.

Lift the cope and turn it horizontal before you swing it over the drag so that any loose sand will fall clear.

Set the cope firmly on the drag without jarring it, and you are ready to pour.

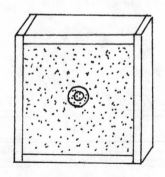

POUR THE MOLD

Review the safety rules for firing the furnace and for handling molten metal before you melt.

Set the mold reasonably level on the sand bed near the furnace. When you pour a number of molds they should be arranged so that you can reach them all while moving forward. Leave nothing in the way to stumble on.

None of the molds in this series of projects need to be weighted or clamped, but larger molds poured in brass or pot metal may need such treatment.

Turn off the air blast when you are satisfied that the metal has reached a temperature that will keep it fluid until the mold is filled. Remove the furnace lid and set it on a couple of bricks near the furnace.

You can stir the melt gently, but don't agitate it. A pine stick is said to flux the melt by introducing rosin, but I can't say I've seen any benefit from it. You can get some notion of fluidity by stirring though.

If there is thick dross on the top you should press it to one side of the pot to wring it out before you skim it off the melt. If the dross is thin you need only push it away from the lip before pouring.

Grasp the pot very firmly, and make sure it can't slip out of the tongs before you lift it. If you can't get the tongs on the pot, you can lift it from the furnace with a pair of long angle nosed pliers and set it on the lid. Be sure your gloves or mitts are thick enough to protect your hands from the radiant heat. Then you can get the tongs on firmly. Hold the pouring lip as near as possible to the sprue and pour steadily, without stopping, until the mold is full to the top of the sprue. If you interrupt pouring the casting will probably fail. Keep the sprue choked with metal until it is completely full.

If the mold is too wet it will begin to boil and bubble in the sprue as soon as it is near full. Stop pouring and step away a few feet until it quiets down. The casting will probably be worthless. Don't attempt to re-pour.

If the metal begins to run out at the parting just stop pouring. If it ignites the flask or the molding board you can toss some sand on it to smother the fire. DON'T THROW WATER ON MOLTEN METAL.

There may be a sound like frying eggs as you pour, and lots of steam and gas, but nothing violent should happen.

Pour left over metal into an ingot mold.

SHAKING OUT THE CASTING

Such a light casting will solidify in just a few minutes, but it will be too hot to handle for some time. It
is best to leave it in the mold until it is cool enough to
handle, but 15 minutes is long enough to wait in this case.
Larger castings can remain fluid for some time, so be sure
that it has solidified before you move the mold.

You are anxious to see the results of your first mold,
so wait 15 or 20 minutes and carry the mold back to the sand
bin. Wear gloves or mitts as you lift the cope and shake it
out into the riddle. Grasp the sprue with long pliers and
set the casting aside as you riddle the sand back into the
bin. Riddle the drag sand back into the bin too, and clean
up the flask before you put it away. Break up the baked
lumps of sand that are left in the riddle, and sprinkle a
bit of water on to re-temper it for the next use. Mix it
in with the rest of the sand.

By now the casting will have cooled a bit and you can
look it over. Don't force cool it in any way.

WHAT WENT WRONG?

It is most likely that the casting will be bright as a
new dime, solid and faithful in detail. All you have to do
is cut off the gates with a hack saw and finish it with a
coarse double cut file and you have a pair of core plates.

There might be 50 things that could go wrong, and after
taking precautions against all of them you may find there
are 51 things that could go wrong. Aluminum and pot metal
are really very easy to work with. Your problems, if any,
will be with molding and pattern practice. If you use clean
scrap, skim before you pour and pour steadily, keeping the
sprue choked with metal, there is little more you can do
about the metal except control the temperature.

Bubbles or voids are caused by trapped steam and gas.
You rammed too hard, you forgot to vent or the sand is a
bit too wet.

The sand will yield from pressure in the mold if you
fail to ram hard enough, and the casting will bulge.

Sand that is too dry, or lacks enough clay for good
bond, will wash into the mold and mix with the metal.

We could go on, these observations are little more than
common sense. A critical examination of your castings is
going to teach you in a way that you will not forget.

CASTING A BALL CRANK HANDLE IN POT METAL

Items like pulleys, hand wheels, ball cranks and bearings are especially easy to make with pot metal because you can use a steel core to form the bore. This eliminates machining, and since we do not yet have a machine shop it is a great help and savings.

The steel core is a mandrel of the same size as the shaft on which the casting is to be mounted. It's coated with graphite or smoked with a candle flame so it won't be bonded to the casting. The core is driven out when the casting has cooled, and the result is a near perfect fit. The same method can be used to form threads that are durable enough for many purposes.

when you begin to build your machine tools you will be needing some ball cranks for feeds and adjustments. They are difficult to find, and very expensive if you are able to find anything near the size you need. These will be as durable as any you can buy, and the cost is very slight.

You can cast them in aluminum in the same way, but they will not be quite as strong.

Make patterns of wood to the sizes below, and you will find them useful as you build your shop. Macrame beads and dowel rod are handy materials for making such patterns.

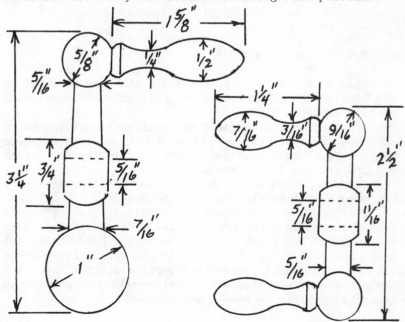

MAKE A ONE PIECE PATTERN

There are alternate methods for molding such a figure,
but a one piece pattern is the practical way for a small
quantity of any one item. We'll discuss some of the alter-
nates later.

Prepare the pattern and slip a dowel through the bore
as seen below. The protruding ends of the dowel form the
core prints, in which the steel core will be layed when the
pattern is drawn from the sand.

CORE PRINTS

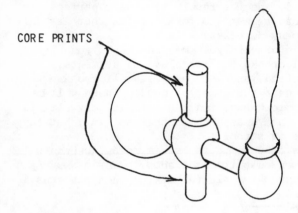

MOLIDNG THE BALL CRANK

Because there is no flat surface that can be layed on
the molding board, the technique is slightly different than
molding the core plates.

A blank drag is prepared by dusting the molding board
and inverting the drag over it as though you were going to
ram up a pattern. Then ram in the sand in layers just as
you did for the core plate mold.

Rub in a bottom board and roll over the drag to expose
the smooth flat parting face of the drag.

This process is called simple bedding. The pattern is
simply rapped into the parting face of the drag until half
is bedded in the sand, and the remaining half is exposed
above the sand. It's important to bed the pattern so that
its largest dimensions are on the parting plane of the mold.
You can use a small trowel to tool around the pattern so
the parting plane is smooth and clean.

Molds are always fed at the heaviest portion, so press a 1" sprue pin about 1/2" into the sand very close to the large ball end. Dust the parting face all over.

Now you can set the cope in place and ram it up in the usual manner.

When the cope has been rammed up and struck off you can pull the sprue pin and prepare the sprue opening to a funnel shape. Open the mold to draw the pattern.

Swab the pattern and rap it lightly, and lift it from the mold. Push the vent wire through the ball areas and the handle stem, and set the steel core in the prints.

Clean up the cavity and parting face, cut the gate, and swab the bottom of the sprue before you close up to pour.

Close up the mold firmly but gently, and pour rapidly with aluminum or pot metal.

The casting is seen below as it is shaken out of the mold. It remains only to cut off the gate and clean up the fins, all of which is done with a hack saw and file.

The steel core is struck in one direction to loosen it, and it is easily driven out the opposite way. Install the set screw, and the job is done.

CHOOSE THE EASIEST METHOD

The core plates and the ball crank are just two examples of molding and pattern practice. All methods involve
the same general ramming, venting and gating, but the difference lies in forming the pattern and bedding it in the
mold. When only one or a few of an item is to be cast it
is not usually worth the time to make a complex pattern,
and most items can be molded by one of the methods seen in
these two simple examples. We'll use some more intricate
patterns as we build the machines, so we'll discuss them
briefly here.

SPLIT PATTERNS

Such shapes as the ball crank must be parted in the mold
at the broadest dimension. they have draft both above and
below the parting plane. These patterns can be split at the
broadest dimension for easier molding. The two halves are
aligned by small pins. One portion is layed on its flat
parting surface and a drag is rammed over it. The drag is
rolled over, and the second part of the pattern is set on to
ram up the cope. When the mold is opened you will have a
part of the pattern in the drag and the other in the cope.
Each part is rapped and removed separately, and the mold is
gated and finished in the usual manner.

COPING DOWN

Making a split pattern can be avoided in some cases by
ramming the pattern into the drag, and then cutting away
the sand to slope toward the practical parting plane. The
parting face of the cope will conform to the face of the
drag. Many irregular shapes can be molded by coping down.

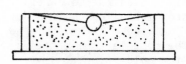
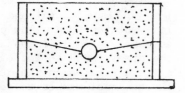

FOLLOW BOARDS

In some cases a special molding board can be prepared that will accept a protruding part of the pattern in a hole or recess. In this way, only the portion of the pattern below the parting plane is bedded in the drag. When the drag is rolled over the follow board is removed, and then the remaining part of the pattern is rammed in the cope. It is a more reliable method than simple bedding.

A FALSE COPE

One problem with simple bedding is that the pattern may remain in the cope when you open the mold. The cavity in the drag will probably be damaged. This happens in the case of small, light patterns like the ball crank.

A false cope is prepared just as you did the blank drag, but the cope is rammed up blank instead. The pattern is rapped in and the parting plane is carefully prepared. then the drag is rammed up over the false cope. The mold is rolled over and opened, and the false cope is shaken out. The sprue pin is set and a new cope is rammed over the drag to complete the mold in the usual manner.

This method also avoids having the sand more firmly packed under the pattern due to rapping it in.

A SAND MATCH

A sand match can be made in a dummy flask, or even in the floor sand. A smooth flat bed of sand is prepared, and the pattern is rapped in just as for a false cope. The drag is then rammed over the pattern just as with the false cope. when done in a dummy flask it is called an odd side.

A PERMANENT ODD SIDE

The usual molding sand is replaced with a mixture of 10% portland cement and clean sand. It is tempered just like molding sand. The pattern is bedded to the parting, and when cured it makes a permanent match for ramming up the drag. When rolled over, the odd side is lifted and the pattern remains in the drag. The cope is then rammed up in the usual manner to complete the mold.

This is a practical method when a larger number of the same pattern are to be molded.

72

Up to this point a great deal was said about the art of sand casting, and yet the subject has hardly been touched. Large volumes have been written on each phase, and these few pages could hardly pretend to be a complete course of instruction. It provides a good foundation though, and on it you can build your own metal working shop.

the charcoal foundry was born out of frustration and fatigue. Hacksawing, chiseling, welding, filing and grinding are hard work. The results can be discouraging if you have to start over again and again. With castings, all of the work is done on nice soft wood when you make the pattern, and if you spoil a casting you just melt it down and do it over. Little is lost but a few minutes and a bit of dust, and once perfected you can make as many as you want of the same item with little cost or effort.

The best way to learn about casting is to make castings. Like all of the manual arts, it is self instructing. Make a pattern and mold it and pour it. An examination of the result will teach you more than you can learn with an entire library of books.

You can devise a series of projects to build some wood working equipment for pattern making. Combine aluminum and pot metal castings with plywood to build a table saw, disc sander or even a sturdy wood lathe.

There are dozens of useful items for the shop that can be made from castings, and they will cost little more than the time it takes to make them. Even more valuable is the skill and knowledge you gain with each experience.

It will be a help to read other books about casting, even if you don't intend to go much beyond these simple methods. Several top notch manuals are available from C. W. Ammen, PO Box 288, Manitou Springs, Colo 80829.

Lindsay Publications, PO Box 12, Bradley, IL 60915, offers an amazing selection of books and manuals on foundry and many other shop topics.

My main offering to the hobbiest and experimenter is a low cost machine shop built from scrap metal. These simple methods and materials are far more practical than you may have thought, and once you have built the foundry and the lathe there will be little to prevent you from having just about any piece of equipment you may want. The cost is slight, and the education and experience that you will gain is beyond any price.

CONCLUSION

If you are entirely new to metal working you may feel just a bit intimidated by the scope of these projects. I hope that won't prevent you from making a start, because these methods are just as easy as they look, and you really can build your own equipment at very low cost.

The series is progressive. You start with nearly nothing, and you use it to produce what is needed as you do each project. Even before it is finished, the lathe will be doing much of the work to produce its own parts. there is nothing deeply technical, and each part is dealt with separately from pattern to finished casting. Taken one step at a time it is hardly more difficult than putting a kit of parts together.

The metal shaper below was built by Paul Nemecek of Springfield, Mo.. Paul made a number of improvements in the design, including ball bearings for the crank shaft. He has a large commercially built lathe, but I built mine with only the small home made lathe, seen in the photo on page 5 of this manual.

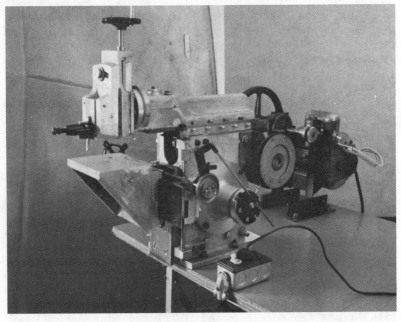

THE METAL SHAPER, BOOK 3

When you have established your foundry and built the lathe and the shaper you will have a full understanding of metal casting and machine work. The milling machine will add a new dimension to your shop.

THE MILLING MACHINE, BOOK 4

The miller is generally considered a luxury in the home shop, but you can have one for little more than the time it takes to build it. Its lathe like characteristics, along with included accessories, enable you to do large diameter work that is beyond the range of the small lathe. It has a compound slide, an angle plate, and it can even make its own milling cutters.

This phase in the project signals the end of tedious work like hand scraping, and finishing flat surfaces now becomes a pleasure instead of a dreaded chore.

It will cut gears, sprockets, splines, key ways, mill slots, cut a dovetail slide or any of dozens of jobs that most home shop operators can only dream about. This is the project to tackle if you already have a lathe.

the drill press may be the most challenging project in the series, because it uses the absolute limit of the cap-acity of the home made lathe. You can handle it though, because you have built the required equipment and acquired the skill and knowledge in earlier projects. All of the castings can be machined on the home made lathe.

THE DRILL PRESS, BOOK 5

You could buy a drill press easily, but that only takes money. What you really need is the skill and knowledge you will gain from building one. I can think of no metal project that will expand your ability better than this one.

The drill press will become your most used machine as you proceed to add refinements to your shop. Firm support and an accurately guided spindle and feed will be vital for the projects that are to follow.

No amateur machinist is content until he has cut gears and done the more exotic jobs that require accurate dividing, but few home shops are ever equipped with a worm wheel dividing head. You will still want to add change gears to the lathe, and your shop will not really be complete until you have a dividing head. It serves as a rotary table for

76

the drill press too, and it indexes the fraction plates for accurate drilling. This will be your most prized piece of equipment, and there is no thrill to compare with cutting your own gears.

THE DIVIDING HEAD, BOOK 6

Book 6 also includes a four jaw chuck, a center rest, a complete set of change gears for the lathe and many items of shop tooling and equipment to complete your shop.

All of this is done by shaping blocks of wood into the simple patterns and ramming them into the sand. The finishing operations are really no more difficult than wood working, and simple hand tools are all you need to start. If you take it just one step at a time, you will quickly see what a really capable workman you are. When you have finished building your shop you will have traced the foot steps of the pioneers of the machine tool industry, and your reward will be a metal working shop that you have built. It is likely that you have much of what is needed on hand right now, so let's get started. You are bound to have fun as you build your own metal working shop from scrap.

APPENDIX

SUPPLY SOURCES

These listings are not adds. I don't recieve any fee or consideration for listeng them. They are companies that have filled orders for me, or that have answered my inquiry.

Campbell Tools Co., 2100 Selma Road, Springfield, Ohio 45505. An excellent listing of supplies and tools for the home metal worker. Fast, personal service. Top quality at very fair prices. Catalog fee: $1.00

Manhattan Supply Company, 151 Sunnyside Blvd., Plainview, Long Island, N. Y. 11803. A large catalog of over 500 pages, listing a full line of industrial quality shop items. Affordable for the home shop. Modest minimum order. catalog fee: $5.00

McKilligan Industrial And Supply Corp., 435 Main St., Johnson City, N. Y. 13790-1998. A 700 page catalog lists a full range of shop supplies and tools, including foundry tools and supplies. Catalog fee: $5.00

Pyramid Products Co., 3736 S. 7th Ave., Phoenix, Arizona 85041. Gas fired melting furnaces and all basic foundry equipment and supplies for the home shop.

Stock Drive Products, 55 South Denton Ave., New Hyde-Park, N. Y. 11040. A 750 page catalog/manual of standard mechanical components. Gears, sprockets, belt drives and some unique mechanical components. An excellent source, and the manual is a valuable reference. $5.95, post paid.

Wholesale Tool Co. Inc., 12155 Stephens Drive, Box 68, Warren, Michigan 48090. A 150 page catalog of machines, tools and supplies. Special pricing on surplus and close-out merchandise. Many hard to find items. Fast service. Four large warehouses. Catalog fee: $1.00

Home Shop Machinist, PO Box 1810, Traverse City, Mich. 49685. Very fine, project oriented magazine. Excellent photography and quality articles, and it's your line of contact with advertizers who can serve home shop needs. One year subscription: $17.50.

The complete " Metal Shop From Scrap " series is designed for the serious hobbiest in metal who can't justify the cost of commercially manufactured equipment for his
home based hobby activity.

The entire series is listed below. With the exception
of the sheet metal brake, all of them require castings in
aluminum or pot metal.

BOOK 1.　THE CHARCOAL FOUNDRY

BOOK 2.　THE METAL LATHE

BOOK 3.　THE METAL SHAPER

BOOK 4.　THE MILLING MACHINE

BOOK 5.　THE DRILL PRESS

BOOK 6.　THE DIVIDNG HEAD & DELUXE ACCESSORIES

BOOK 7.　DESIGNING & BUILDING THE SHEET METAL BRAKE

The sheet metal brake is a welding project, using standard structural steel and fasteners to build a compact port-
able bending brake.

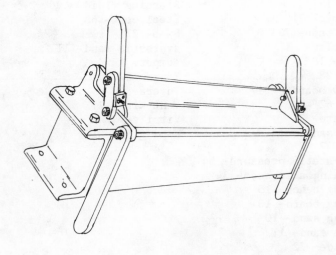